THE GREAT
HOUDINI'S
PUZZLE VAULT

THIS IS A SEVENOAKS BOOK

Published in 2017 by SevenOaks
An imprint of the Carlton Publishing Group
20 Mortimer Street
London W1T 3JW

10 9 8 7 6 5 4 3 2 1

ISBN 978-1-78177-752-7

10 9 8 7 6 5 4 3 2 1

Editorial Director: Roland Hall
Design Manager: Stephen Cary
Picture Research: Steve Behan
Production: Lisa Cook

The publishers would like to thank the following sources for their kind permission to reproduce
photographs and illustrations in this book:

Alamy, Dover Books, Getty Images, Mary Evans Picture Library and Shutterstock.

Every effort has been made to acknowledge correctly and contact the source and/or copyright
holder of each picture and Carlton Books Limited apologizes for any unintentional errors or
omissions, which will be corrected in future editions of this book.

Printed in China.

THE GREAT
HOUDINI'S
PUZZLE VAULT

A COLLECTION OF
MYSTIFYING PUZZLES
INSPIRED BY THE
ASTOUNDING ESCAPOLOGIST

TIM DEDOPULOS

SEVENOAKS

CONTENTS

INTRODUCTION

HARRY HOUDINI is still remembered as probably the greatest illusionist and escapologist to have lived, and he definitely remains the most famous. His is a household name, synonymous with daring escapes. Even today, stage magic and escapology are shaped by his legacy of daring, cunning and dogged perfectionism.

Houdini was born in 1874 as Erik Weisz, the son of Jewish parents who lived in Budapest in Hungary. The family moved to America in 1878, and found their way to New York in 1887. His stage name, Houdini, was homage to Jean-Eugène Robert-Houdin, the father of modern stage magic. He started out with strong-man and card-trick acts, and met his wife and life-long stage partner Bess Rahner during this time. But Houdini's true expertise, born of fascination and years of intensive study, was with handcuffs. His friend and manager Martin Beck noticed, and steered him into escapology. From there, his career exploded into glory.

Fame found Houdini concentrating primarily on escaping from handcuffs, straitjackets, chains and ropes, on stages, in jails, underwater, and even dangling from on high. His incredible physical tone allowed many potentially lethal feats to be performed in perfect safety. After a time, to stay ahead of imitators, he began specializing in escaping from various contraptions and containers, many of them water-filled for an extra dash of lethal danger. These spectacles elevated him to the level of highest-paid vaudeville entertainer in the USA.

In addition to his dazzling stage shows, Houdini also found time to work as the visionary president of the Society of American Magicians. He was a compulsive evangelist for stage magic and magic societies, and grew the S.A.M. from a tiny New York backroom meet to an international powerhouse. He also starred in movies, took up pioneer aviation for a time, worked tirelessly to expose fraudulent mediums, and even published a (rather ranty) magazine for a couple of issues.

This volume draws inspiration from right across Houdini's legacy, rooting puzzles in both the spirit of escape from difficult situations, and in the details and techniques behind some of Houdini's most famous perfomances. There are also puzzles based on other areas of stage magic with which he would have worked. But escapology, of course, is the heart of Houdini's enchantment. Just remember that, like the other branches of stage magic, escapology relies mainly on deception. You'll need to bring a twisty mind and a wary eye to these brainteasers if you hope to puzzle them out.

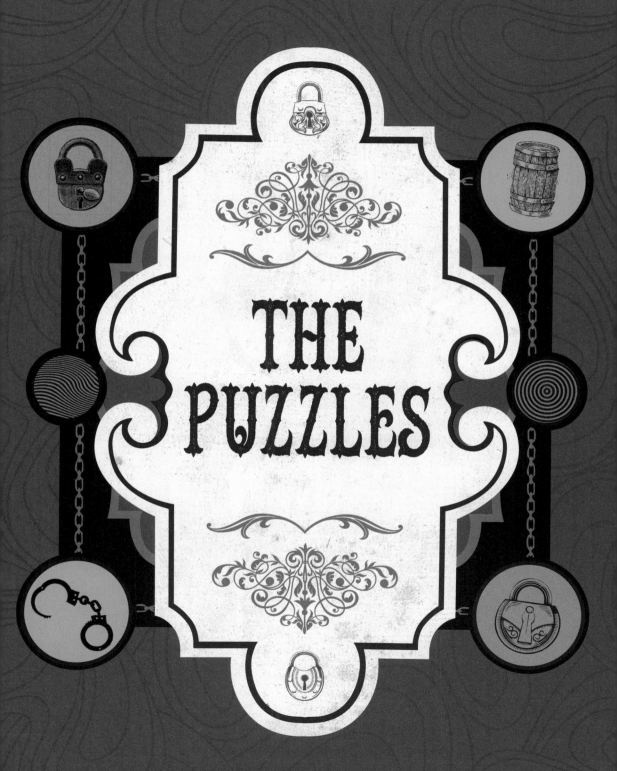

THE PUZZLES

THE ESCAPE

Part One

I WAKE SLOWLY, my mind and body unusually sluggish, my surroundings unfamiliar. *Where am I? How did I get here?* My memory offers no answers. I'm no stranger to endless hotel rooms, but this place is utterly unknown to me. We're not on tour, either. I should be at home. Where is Bess?

This is an outrage.

Glancing around the room, my eyes alight upon a piece of paper tacked to the back of the door. I get up off bed and walk over to it, to see what it has to say.

Well, now. There seems little option but to take the matter at face value, at least for the now. Questions tumble over themselves in my mind, but there is no one to whom they might be addressed, and in honesty the most pressing problem has already been clearly laid out for my attention.

The first order of business is to try the door. Never believe what you are told when illusion is at play. In this instance however, the information is solid. The door handle refuses to turn, even under duress. There is no keyhole or other unlocking mechanism visible anywhere on the door in fact, so my first thoughts of contriving a lock-pick must be set aside.

The door appears of ordinary construction. It is fashioned of stout dark wood, and fits its frame snugly. It opens inwards, as shown by the simple mortise butt hinges visible. The handle is shaped like a sphere, and from its slight amount of play, would turn horizontally were the door unlocked. Doors with locks on only one side are not common, but I have come across them before. There is nothing to suggest that this is not a normal example of the type.

I remove my captor's note, and insinuate it between door and frame. I then run it around the entire door. There is the resistance one would expect of a lock-bolt, located a little below the handle, but otherwise nothing. So it seems reasonable to assume that there are no further security bolts extending from the door into the frame, say at the top or bottom.

To The Great Houdini,

Please forgive the imposition. Do not be alarmed, sir. Your wife is safe at home, and you are not in any pressing danger. This door is, of course, locked, and the key is elsewhere. However, we are confident that a man of your talents will not find it excessively problematic to facilitate a convenient means of egress without resorting to wanton destruction.

Be certain, sir, that we hold you in the highest regard.

Sincerely yours, Q

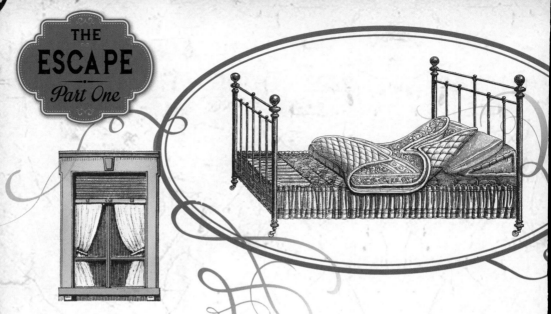

THE
ESCAPE
Part One

With that matter settled, I turn my attention to the rest of the room. The primary feature is a single-sleeper bed, around six feet long and three-and-a-half feet wide, pleasantly made up with mattress, sheets, blanket, and down pillows in slip cases. It has a cast-iron frame, including bars at the head and foot. The frame has been welded into one piece, and has a slat-like base. The mattress is sprung, and a close examination reveals a tear in the fabric through which a spring might plausibly be coaxed. Would that be considered wanton? I *think* not.

There are decorative knobs on the four bedpost corners that appear to be screwed in place. I test one and yes, it will unfasten. The knobs are solid chunks of brass, it seems, of a size to fit comfortably in the palm of my hand. That is a piece of information worth bearing in mind, I suppose. Small feathers could also undoubtedly be pried from the pillows without any particular destruction proving necessary, should a use for such things manifest itself. Truly, the smallest details sometimes are the most critical. The pair of bed-sheets could each be twisted into ropes about eight-and-one-half feet in length. The same is true of the blanket, although it would be thicker and would bear less weight, as wool is far less tightly spun than cotton.

Thought of ropes leads me naturally to the window. It is located directly above the head of the bed, and covered with thick curtains. These are sturdy, and each of them could easily add another six feet of makeshift rope. Wooden rings a half-inch thick and some three inches in diameter attach the fabric to a pole, which rests on metal hooks screwed into the wall. Disassembly would be simple, and being trivially reversible, I feel comfortable in deciding that such a course would not constitute an act of destruction. The fabric loops that hold the rings on the curtains are simple flaps whose stitching could be unpicked.

Opening the curtain leaves me dismayed, however. There is a window frame, but no window to accompany it! It is simply a large rectangle of wood which has been nailed to the wall, and then the curtains are hung over it. The wallpaper is visibly continuous beneath it. A vexing surprise. I rap my knuckles on the fake window, but it is definitely stone beneath the wallpaper, like the rest of the wall. Someone has gone to great pains for my supposed benefit. The frame does not appear to be nailed to the wall with any particular conviction, and prising it loose without destroying it ought to be possible. That would probably free up several small nails, for use in ... well, nothing leaps to mind.

On the opposite side of the room from the door, where one would normally expect to find a washbasin, there is a drinks cabinet. An intriguing deviation from the norm. Perhaps my captors feel I might be swayed to a tipple, hampering my efforts to escape. But then perhaps I am being uncharitable, and they merely seek to be hospitable. On top of a pleasant oak cabinet with glass-paned doors rests four tumblers, a quart jug of apparent water, and a bucket of slightly melted ice cubes, complete with a slim steel ice pick, hickory-handled, and a delicate pair of tongs. Beside the bucket is a porcelain bowl about the width of my spread hand, which contains a generous measure of peanuts.

Inside the cabinet are bottles of Scotch whisky, bourbon, gin, brandy, rum, vodka and tequila. The tops could be removed from all of these, should that seem necessary – the brandy and rum have cork stoppers set inside plastic seals, whilst the others have screw tops. There is also a cut crystal decanter of wine, judging by its scent a Merlot. This too is stoppered, with a chunk of cut crystal that matches the decanter.

All in all, it is not a piece that one would expect to find in a bedroom.

A short distance from the foot of the bed, against the remaining wall, there is an attractively designed writing desk, with a wingback chair. The space between chair and bed looks somewhat cramped. Is this room normally an office of some sort? The lack of cupboards and the artificial window both go some way towards supporting the idea.

Desk and chair are both upholstered in a tasteful forest-green leather which is fastened in place by brass rivets or the like. The desk bears a green-shaded reading lamp of the art deco style, along with a bottle of India ink, a black-barrelled fountain pen with a gold nib, a small stack of blotting paper, and a black, hardbound ledger with red trim. I seize on the ledger, but am unsurprised to find it empty. I would not leave information lying around in such a carefully prepared situation, either.

There is little else to add. Illumination comes from an overhead light whose switch I cannot spy. It has a cloth shade in a soft orange colour which may be removable if necessary. The floor appears to be boards of oak, polished with beeswax to a warm, mellow shine. The reading lamp is connected to a regular electrical outlet, and turns on and off when I flick its switch accordingly. The desk has three drawers, but all are empty save for pieces of stiff paper which are clearly there to provide a liner.

I look around the room again, one final time, and nod to myself in satisfaction. I should be out of here in under two minutes.

Can you see how?

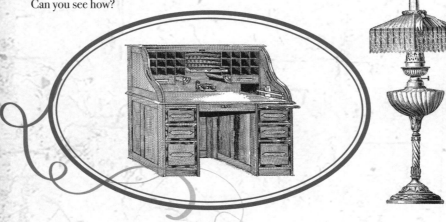

SOLUTION ON PAGE 166

THREADING
The NEEDLE

To ENSURE THE safety of magic tricks and escapes, it is always of vital importance to have exact control over and information on the materials to be used. There is a myriad of useful little techniques that help in this matter.

For example, consider the matter of a cylindrical steel barrel to be half-filled with water. It is quite possible that for certain tricks, underestimating the amount of water in the barrel could prove to be a fatal error. Similarly, whilst overestimating the water level is unlikely to be dangerous, it could easily render a trick obvious, to the disappointment of the audience.

Given such a barrel – open-topped for the now – can you think of a simple way to ascertain for certain whether it is more or less than half-full without the assistance of a measuring aid or other tool?

SOLUTION ON PAGE 166

THE WALK
of PENANCE

THE GREAT HOUDINI takes to the stage. With a flourish, he beckons to some burly assistants. These worthies carry on a long metal trench, which they place in front of the illusionist. While they retreat, Houdini tips the trench up to show it to the audience. It is roughly eighteen inches wide, four inches deep, and six feet in length, made from plates of steel welded together. The assistants return, each carrying boxes, which they empty into the trench. With a great clattering and shattering, shards of broken glass pour out of the boxes and into the trench, filling it completely.

Whilst the Great Houdini removes his finery, stripping down to a pair of well-padded swimming trunks, the audience is invited to come and inspect the contents of the metal container. It is indeed as it appears to be – genuine pieces of broken glass, from a number of window panes by the look of it.

Once all are re-seated, Houdini produces a small step box, and walks from that onto the glass. As the audience winces, he slowly walks the length of the trench, groaning in pain at every step. At the far end, he turns and starts walking back. About halfway along, he actually slowly lowers himself and lies down on his back, his body entirely within the trench. The largest of the assistants steps forward, moves the step to a point near the magician, then climbs from it to stand on the great man's very stomach.

As the audience members scream, the assistant steps back, and Houdini carefully rises, and steps out of the trench. He turns his back to the crowd – and is unharmed.

What is the secret?

SOLUTION ON PAGE 167

HANDCUFFS

HOUDINI had a number of signature acts, and one of the earliest of these was his boast that he was able to escape from any pair of handcuffs provided by either the audience or local police. The act was so impressive that it gave him his first break in 1899, winning him a tour of the US.

But how did he do it? I'll give you a tip – it didn't involve dislocating his thumb.

SOLUTION ON PAGE 167

ESCAPE
THE MAZE

START

END

SOLUTION ON PAGE 168

EXPERTISE

IN THIS DAZZLING display of talent and psychic ability, the Great Houdini sets up chessboards for a row of four opponents, and then places a folded scrap of paper on a desk, in the care of an adjudicator.

Once all is ready, the games begin. Houdini is a whirlwind of motion as he starts off the chess games, moving from board to board, playing ferociously against his cunning opponents. He takes white on each board of course, and seems to never need more than a moment refreshing himself to find a move that leaves his opponent reeling. The adjudicator has his work cut out just ensuring that all moves are legal.

Pieces fall like dominoes, and in less than five minutes all four games are done. Houdini has won two, drawn a third, and lost the fourth. But the best is yet to come. After congratulating his opponents, he moves to the adjudicator, and asks the man to pick up the scrap of paper and read the number inside. The adjudicator does as asked, and is stunned to discover that the number is exactly equal to the number of pieces left on all four boards.

Assuming that the chess matches are unscripted and the adjudicator is not in on the act, how is this possible?

SOLUTION ON PAGE 168

NAILED

A **LARGE MASONRY** nail, thick and gleaming, is shown to the audience, rapped on a table, and pushed through a piece of fruit. The Great Houdini makes it perfectly clear that the nail is normal in all respects. Then he takes a paper cup, and pushes the nail up through the base, so that it points straight upwards towards the top. With that done, he covers the cup with a simple lid, and places it on the table. Three more cups follow, so that there are four identical covered cups.

Whilst Houdini turns his back, his assistant mixes the cups up, shuffling them thoroughly until a volunteer from the audience tells her to stop. Then the magician turns back around, and the volunteer selects one of the four cups.

Without hesitation, Houdini slams his palm down on the chosen cup. Bam! The cup is flattened. Again, he demands a choice of cups. Awed and shaken, the volunteer picks a second cup. Bam! Again, Houdini flattens the cup with his hand. The magician looks out to the audience for a long moment, then thoughtfully asks for a final selection. Bam! Once more, the cup is flattened, and the magician is unharmed. He snatches up the last cup, dismantles it, and produces the nail to demonstrate to the audience once more.

The volunteer is genuine, and has no idea which cup is which. How can Houdini risk this trick?

SOLUTION ON PAGE 169

BLOWN AWAY

PRODUCING A DECK of cards, the Great Houdini shuffles it thoroughly and calls for a volunteer. The person chosen is genuinely not in on the act. Whilst the magician closes his eyes and turns his head to the side, he riffles through the cards, showing them to the volunteer, who is asked to choose one as she sees it go past. The volunteer does so, but does not tell Houdini that she has done so until the entire pack is riffled.

The magician then puts the deck back down, and tunes in psychically. As the bemused volunteer looks on, he identifies her card: "I'm getting a high card, yes, definitely high, is it red? No, black, that's right. Court cards, no. Evenness is ... out, I think... Nine of Clubs!"

As the volunteer gasps in shock, Houdini picks the deck back up and riffles it slowly out in front of her. To her amazement, the Nine of Clubs is no longer in the deck.

How is this possible?

SOLUTION ON PAGE 169

SPOT THIS

THE GREAT HOUDINI has concealed 10 differences in the opposite picture. Can you find them?

SOLUTION ON PAGE 170

MIND
The TANK

WHEN PERFORMING ILLUSIONS involving the use of water, it's vitally important to have a solid understanding of fluid dynamics. You have to know exactly how water is going to behave under every possible circumstance before risking your life by voluntarily locking yourself away in a water-filled compartment.

To that end, consider this situation. You have a tank of water, with markings up the side allowing you to clearly see the level that the water is at. You place a watertight steel bucket inside the tank. It floats, as expected, and the water level increases, again as expected. Next, you place a fist-sized stone in the bucket. The bucket sinks a bit, and the water level rises further.

You make a precise note of that level, then remove the stone from the bucket and instead drop it straight into the tank. It sinks, like the stone it is. When the water settles, is its level now higher or lower than it was when you noted it?

SOLUTION ON PAGE 171

RIVER RUN

ONCE THE CHALLENGE of escaping from handcuffs became too simple, the Great Houdini started spicing it up by having his hands cuffed behind his back before then jumping off a bridge into a river. For these performances, he wore only a close-fitting pair of trunks, and was unable to hide a handcuff key anywhere useful where it could both be guaranteed to stay close to his hands and also pass his and his handcuffs' pre-jump close inspection by his awed volunteers.

Even so, he would invariably break free of the tightly applied cuffs in a matter of seconds after hitting the water. Then it was just a case of staying down long enough to start worrying the spectators before making his triumphant return to the surface.

But how did he do it? The answer still doesn't involve dislocating his thumb.

SOLUTION ON PAGE 171

HEARTBEAT

As preparation for a dangerous stunt, one that gives the impression of involving probable injury, the Great Houdini announces that he will minimize the risk of blood loss by stopping his heart from beating. An incredible claim, to be sure. To help prove this, a volunteer with some first-aid training or other medical knowledge is sought from the audience.

When the volunteer is up on the stage, the magician pulls up his right sleeve, and hands the newcomer his wrist. Once she confirms that she has found his pulse, Houdini closes his eyes and concentrates, slowing his breathing. Incredibly, his pulse begins to slow and fade. Within a matter of seconds, it vanishes completely. The volunteer confirms, quite honestly, that his pulse has stopped.

If I tell you that no special bodily training is required to duplicate this feat, can you say how it is done?

SOLUTION ON PAGE 171

START

END

SOLUTION ON PAGE 172

INVISIBLE
TOUCH

❧◦◦◦ ◦•◦◦◦❧

A SMALL GROUP of genuine volunteers are called up on to the stage, and the Great Houdini welcomes them, sets them at their ease, and honestly confirms that they neither know him nor each other. He then informs them that he is going to use them to demonstrate his powers of telekinesis, touching them without ever making physical contact.

One of the group is blindfolded so that she can see nothing, and the magician explains how he will be using the power of his mind to touch her arm a certain number of times, very lightly. He shows the rest of the group that he has no hidden devices up his sleeves or in the lining of his jacket. Then he steps back a few paces, screws up his face in ferocious mental effort, and gestures sharply at the volunteer, once, twice, thrice ... four times. He relaxes, takes several deep breaths, then tells the volunteer to remove her blindfold and tell the audience how many touches she felt. "Four," she admits.

How did he manage this feat?

FLOATING

IN HUSHED TONES, the Great Houdini describes the years of intense mystical training required to attain his next feat – defying gravity itself and floating up off the very ground. It is an ancient technique, he explains, passed on in secret from master to student, and he had to undergo many stringent tests in order to be found worthy of the knowledge.

With that said, the magician turns side-on to give the audience a better view, brings his feet together, and opens his arms wide. Breathing deeply, he slowly rises up off the floor until he is floating several inches in the air. The audience can clearly see his feet pressed together, hovering in the air. Then he slowly lowers again, and relaxes.

An impressive feat. How is it done, given that wires and other such devices are not involved?

SOLUTION ON PAGE 173

WIRE WALKER

CENTRE OF GRAVITY is another vitally important tool in the arsenal of any illusionist intent on performing physical feats. Once you're moving around, it comes into play in any number of critical ways.

The most obvious example is high-wire acrobatics which, while not strictly speaking illusionism, feature in the acts of several of the more daring magicians. A common prop amongst wire-walkers is a very long stick which droops down at the ends, indicating the presence of heavy weights at either end.

How is this of use?

SOLUTION ON PAGE 173

CELL

ONE OF THE Great Houdini's more popular feats was to escape from some of the most infamously secure prisons in the world. While this stunt could hardly be performed in front of audiences, it thrilled journalists, who filled pages with their stunned accounts of Houdini's ability to defeat seemingly any security.

Sometimes the prison staff set extra challenges to add some difficulty. In Massachusetts, Houdini didn't just escape from handcuffs in a locked Boston City Prison cell; he scaled the prison walls and ran half a mile to get to a telephone call with the superintendent, all in under twenty minutes. In Washington DC, he didn't just escape his own cell, he shuffled around eight other prisoners so each ended up in a different cell to the one he'd started in.

How did Houdini get out of all those prison cells, when lock-picks wouldn't work on them, and the keys were in the possession of the warders?

SOLUTION ON PAGE 173

HARRY HOUDINI

KING OF CARDS

NATIONAL PR. & ENG. CO. CHICAGO

1838

THE GREAT HOUDINI has concealed 10 differences in the opposite picture. Can you find them?

HARRY HOUDINI

KING OF CARDS

NATIONAL PR. & ENG. CO. CHICAGO

SOLUTION ON PAGE 174

FORCING CHOICE

THE GREAT HOUDINI has a willing volunteer up on stage to play a vital part in the proceedings of his next trick. This volunteer is genuinely ignorant of what's going on, rather than being a stooge. Nevertheless, it is important that he should pick the correct item from a tray of three possibilities.

Fortunately, forcing the volunteer to select the correct item is straightforward. To begin, the magician tells his volunteer to pick any two of the three objects available. Can you see how this forces the man down the path to the right choice?

SOLUTION ON PAGE 175

EXIT STRATEGIES

In a thought-provoking display of psychic ability, the Great Houdini calls a volunteer up on stage. This volunteer is innocent of any foreknowledge or collusion. After some introductions to put the volunteer at ease, the magician takes her over to a large table. On the table are three identical dinner plates, apart from the fact that each has a different number written on it, 1, 2 or 3. He explains how he is going to use his powers of mental domination to force the volunteer to choose the plate he wants her to select.

Houdini hands the volunteer a small, tightly folded piece of paper, and tells her to place it on the plate of her choice. She does so, putting it on plate two. Smiling, he tells her to reach beneath the table, and find a sheet of paper taped there. She is stunned when she produces it, for it reads "You will select plate two!"

How could this be possible?

SOLUTION ON PAGE 175

NO PIT

ALTHOUGH PENDULUMS ARE mostly used in mentalism as props to suggest that hypnosis or mesmerism is taking place, they are fascinating devices, and the principles behind their construction are important in all manner of mechanisms and mechanically focussed tricks. As such, it is definitely useful to have a firm understanding of their properties.

So let us assume we have a pair of pendulums, identical in every respect, inside a vacuum jar. They are drawn up to the same height, and set swinging. Being identical, they will remain in perfect synchronization until all their energy is expended. Now repeat the process, but lengthen the string of one and not of the other. When you release them, you will find that the bob on the longer string is now slower. Similarly, if you shortened its string, you would speed it up.

Finally, put the strings back to the same length, but replace the bob of one pendulum with a hollow shell of identical size, so that it is now considerably lighter than the other. What difference will this make?

SOLUTION ON PAGE 175

PUZZLE CHAIN

THE GREAT HOUDINI is caught in a chain of puzzles. To save him, you will have to work your way through the chain, making careful note of your answers to each link. You'll need them all if you're going to successfully open the cunning puzzle lock that binds him. For the greatest challenge, do not check to see if your answers are correct until after you've completed the final lock.

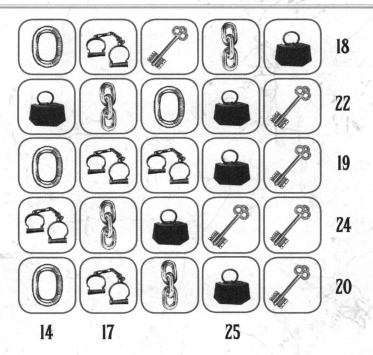

18

22

19

24

20

14   17   25

In this grid, each symbol has a consistent value, and the sums of the values of the symbols in certain rows and columns are given at the end of that line of symbols. Knowing this, what is the minimum value of the symbol in the bottom left? The answer to this gives you the value of the first link in the chain.

SOLUTION ON PAGE 176

SECOND LINK

PUZZLE CHAIN

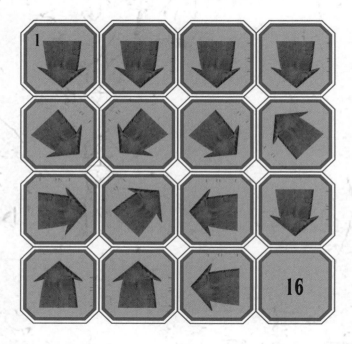

THE AIM of this numeric maze is to work your way from square 1 to square 16, stopping exactly once at each other square on the way. You can move any distance from the square you are on, but only in the precise direction indicated by the arrow.

Number the squares in the sequence you land on them, starting from square 1. The value of the first link in the chain will give you the correct sequence number of the square in the bottom left of the maze.

There is only one correct route. When you have it, check the sequence number of the top right square. This number is the value of the second link in the chain. What is it?

SOLUTION ON PAGE 176

PUZZLE CHAIN

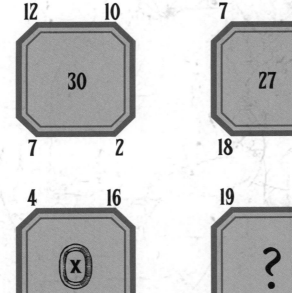

12   10

30

7   2

7   20

27

18   3

4   16

X

9   1

19   15

?

11   2

The values of these squares follow a certain specific logic, if you can uncover it. The value of the second link in the chain will tell you how much X is worth.

The number that should replace the question mark is the value of the third link of the chain. What is it?

SOLUTION ON PAGE 176

PUZZLE CHAIN

7	8	4	4	X	Y
4	1	1	8	5	3
3	7	2	5	9	3

8	4	1	9	1	4
4	9	4	5	3	3
3	4	7	?	?	?

These grids of numbers operate according to a certain logic. If you uncover it, you can figure out what numbers should replace the question marks. The tens digit of the third link's value is equal to the space marked with an X, and the units digit to the Y. Once you have uncovered the correct numbers to replace the question mark, the digit in the bottom right of the second grid gives you the answer to the fourth link.

SOLUTION ON PAGE 176

FINAL LINK

PUZZLE CHAIN

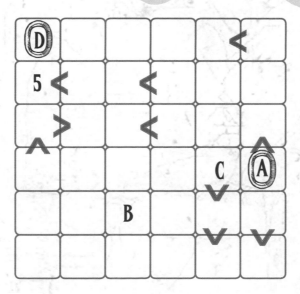

To finally unlock the chain binding the Great Houdini, you have to complete this grid of numbers correctly.

Each row and column of this grid contains the numbers 1-6 once exactly. The chevrons (">" signs) between cells indicate that the number on the wide side of the chevron is larger than the number on the pointed side. In the grid, the letter A represents the value of the first link in the chain, the letter B represents the units digit of the value of the second link in the chain, the letter C represents the tens digit of the value of the third link in the chain, and the letter D represents the value of the fourth link in the chain.

Can you complete the grid and free Houdini?

SOLUTION ON PAGE 177

KEYMASTER

— ·•●◆●•· — ·•◆•· — ·●◆●·•◆•· —

BEFORE EMBARKING ON his jail cell escapes, Houdini was invariably thoroughly searched by the prison staff – people well-practised in making sure that no one was able to smuggle small items past their notice. On occasions where he was permitted to retain his clothing, the matter was simple. A key could be hidden in the lining of a jacket, or the hollow heel of his special shoes. Other times, he employed a cunning "hooked key" that he could attach to the back of someone's clothing with the lightest of touches, and then retrieve after inspection.

Sometimes, however, more rigorous prison staff would insist on stripping the magician down and carefully inspecting him, even to the point of checking beneath his tongue and in between his toes. Even so, he had a hiding place that rarely failed him, given the particular nature of prison inmates.

Can you figure out what it was?

SOLUTION ON PAGE 177

THE
MENTALIST

IN THIS TRICK, a member of the audience is selected – an actual punter, who hasn't been primed in advance. After some introductions and chatter, the Great Houdini informs the man that he will be called upon to make some selections, but he is not to reveal what they are until asked to do so.

First, Houdini asks the man to select any colour. Before he is allowed to reveal his choice though, the magician writes down his psychic perception on a pad of paper, and puts it into a cup. Once that is in place, the man tells everyone his choice.

Secondly, the volunteer is asked to pick a number up to one hundred. Again, Houdini writes down his psychic input, and then the man reveals his pick. Finally, the subject is presented with a selection of three physical objects on a tray, and allowed to pick one of them. This perception too is put into the cup.

After the choices have all been revealed to the audience, the subject is called to the front. The cup of predictions is flamboyantly upended on to a table, and the volunteer reads what has been written, only to discover that the magician has been right every time, no matter how obscure his selections.

But how?

SOLUTION ON PAGE 178

FAMILIARITY

Extra detail is the magician's friend. By drowning every instant in drama and flourish and engaging patter, even the most simple, straightforward scenario can become a thing of confusion and mystery. Do it well, and people will be so mesmerized that they won't notice the things your hands are doing, even without big distractions elsewhere on the stage. But even small amounts of seemingly pertinent but excess detail can provide disproportionate amounts of distraction.

For example, consider a situation where you are talking to a man whose mother is your mother's mother-in-law. What relation is he to you?

SOLUTION ON PAGE 178

EXIT

SOLUTION ON PAGE 179

IN EXTREMIS

VERY RARELY, HOUDINI's every artifice for concealing a key about his person proved ineffective. Since his prison escape challenges often included a forfeit by which he'd remain imprisoned for the night if he was unable to escape, there was a certain note of tension involved in these instances.

On one occasion when the search had been particularly thorough and relentless, Houdini was genuinely locked into a prison cell without a copy of the key anywhere at his disposal. He sportingly admitted his defeat, gave his wife a farewell kiss though the bars and was out five minutes later, much to the annoyance and bafflement of the prison's warden.

How did he do it?

SOLUTION ON PAGE 179

HOUDINI'S CHINESE *Water Torture* CELL

THE MOST SENSATIONAL of Houdini's escape acts was his patented Chinese Water Torture Cell, an oblong aquarium with half-inch-thick glass walls and a steel frame that held almost a thousand litres of water. To start the performance, an audience member was allowed to specify any spot on the stage for the cell to be set up. Once it was in place, people were allowed to inspect the cell, and Houdini had a standing offer for a thousand-dollar reward to anyone who could show that he would have access to oxygen whilst within it.

Houdini then lay down and placed his ankles in a set of mahogany stocks, which were then hauled up into the air on wires, so that he dangled down from them. The cell was filled with water to the brim, and he was lowered into it swiftly. The stocks fitted the cell, acting as a lid, and had four hasps that were locked onto the cell, securing the whole in place.

Drapes were then pulled across the cell, and a brawny assistant took his place in front of them with an axe, ready to smash the glass if needed.

He never was. Two minutes later, the drapes would part to show Houdini safely out of the tank, with the stocks still over the top of the lid, all hasps tightly locked in place.

Can you see how this was achieved?

SOLUTION ON PAGE 186

A PAIN
in the NECK

AN ASSISTANT COMES on to the stage carrying several feet of thick, solid chain, and presents it to the Great Houdini. A pair of genuine audience members are then called up to examine it, and to provide some help for the trick. The chain is very real, and surprisingly heavy. The two volunteers tug at it, and accurately let the rest of the audience know that it's not gimmicked in any way.

Houdini takes the chain back from the men, and places one end carefully over each shoulder, so that it passes in front of his throat. Then he reaches back, pushing his wild hair out of the way for a moment, and loops the chain around his neck. Finally, he passes the loose ends to the two men. Their instructions are simple: on his mark, they are to pull the chain tight as hard as they can. He insists that the chain will pass through his neck without causing any permanent harm.

Once the volunteers reluctantly agree to pull and keep pulling no matter what, he counts down from three. With a massive clatter, the chain snaps taut, still intact, in front of the magician's throat. He collapses with a cry of agony, but recovers shortly afterwards, to show that his neck remains intact.

How?

SOLUTION ON PAGE 180

NEVER FORGET

IN THIS SPECTACULAR trick, a dozen people are selected from the audience to provide assistance. A live elephant is brought on to the stage, and her handler introduces her to the audience and ensures that she is calm.

The Great Houdini gathers up the volunteers, sets them at ease, and has them form a circle around the elephant, holding hands. He joins them to make a large circle of thirteen. The curtain drops, the band plays an impressive fanfare, and when the curtain rises again, Houdini and the twelve volunteers are still in place, but the elephant is no longer inside the circle. Houdini drops the circle to triumphantly run through the space where the elephant was, before returning to take up the hands of the volunteers again.

The curtain drops again, there is another peal of music, and this time, when it rises, the elephant is back in place. No wires or trapdoors are involved in this trick, so where does the elephant go?

SOLUTION ON PAGE 180

CARL DEVO

THE GREAT HOUDINI has concealed 10 differences in the opposite picture. Can you find them?

CARL DEVO

SOLUTION ON PAGE 181

DEATH
ESCAPE

AS THE GREAT Houdini explains to his audience, this is a particularly deadly trick. He asks them to keep silent during the escape, so as to minimize the danger of distraction.

Assistants come on to the stage carrying a range of objects. Two of them, in particular, are sharing a very heavy burden – a large steel weight. One of the assistants steps forward and helps Houdini into a tight straitjacket, fastening him in securely so that he can barely move. Next, chains are wrapped around him, looping around both his torso and ankles, and locked in place. The magician lies down, and the ankle chains are connected to a hoist. Once it is in place, he is lifted up by the feet until he is hanging upside down a foot above the stage.

It is the final piece that makes the trick so lethal. There is a loop of chain wrapped tightly around Houdini's neck, and the two assistants stagger over with their steel weight and lock it firmly onto that section of chain.

As the screen comes across, Bess, his wife, explains nervously that Houdini's strength is great enough to allow him to bear the weight of the chain at his neck for a short time, but in less than a minute, it will surely rip his head clean off his shoulders.

Ninety seconds later, the magician is free, neck intact. How did he avoid at least dislocating his neck bones?

SOLUTION ON PAGE 182

THE BELL

ARE YOU BEGINNING to think like an illusionist yet? Suppose that there is a small church bell that you need to silence for the duration of a performance. During the performance, you will have no access to the bell, and once the show is finished, members of the public will go to examine it. You will have no opportunity to beat them there, so you can't leave any equipment in place or they will surely discover it.

Without resorting to exotic means, can you think of a way to silence the bell for a while? You have the option of as many practice runs as necessary to perfect your technique.

SOLUTION ON PAGE 182

ESCAPE

THE MAZE

START

END

SOLUTION ON PAGE 183

The
VANISHING
ELEPHANT

HOUDINI PERFORMED THIS particular illusion just once, at the New York Hippodrome. As well as having the world's largest stage at the time, the Hippodrome actually had an entire troupe of trained elephants, making it the perfect venue.

As the trainer brought an elephant onto the stage, Houdini explained that he had prepared a simple wooden cabinet, eight square feet in the cross-section, with a cloth front and a hole in the back doors so that the audience could easily see through. Each piece of the cabinet was displayed to the audience before assistants assembled it, so that they could see that each one was just a simple piece of wood.

Once the cabinet was complete, parallel to the stage, the elephant was walked inside, and a team of twelve assistants ponderously rotated the cabinet over the course of several minutes. Once it had been turned, the front curtain was thrown back, and the audience was able to see that the cabinet was empty.

Where did the elephant go?

SOLUTION ON PAGE 183

THERE IS
No SPOON

SHOWING A LARGE, ornately worked silver spoon to the audience, the Great Houdini explains that the item is a miraculous artefact, an heirloom from the old country passed down through the centuries and imbued with mysterious reserves of power. Several members of the audience are selected and brought on to the stage, where they closely examine the spoon and confirm that it is perfectly regular, and a little under a foot long.

The magician then takes hold of the end of the spoon, and covers it in a silk cloth. The audience members are told to line up, and take their time feeling the spoon through the cloth. They do so, readily agreeing that everything is in order. As soon as the last audience member's fingers leave the piece of silk, Houdini whips it into the air. The spoon is gone.

Where did it go?

SOLUTION ON PAGE 184

TRAPEZE

IT'S AN **IMPRESSIVE** feat of daring, the trapeze. As the music ebbs and flows, the highly trained athletes leap and dart through the air, their lives literally in each other's hands. The timing, of course, has to be absolute. The smallest deviation from the routine can prove disastrous, even lethal. When you leap into the void, you have to know your partner's hands will be there to catch you. So trapeze artists rehearse and rehearse.

But expertise is no guarantee of perfection. There are always tiny variations – minor missteps and overbalances, stray gusts of air, and any of a thousand other minuscule confounding factors. It is possible to ameliorate some of the potential chaos through the use of spare moments built into the routine, to give a moment where a minor flaw in timing can be overcome, but even these provide issues of their own. How do you know to judge whether to take three seconds smiling at the crowd, or two and a half?

There is one protection, a technique that ensures most such routines do not collapse under their own weight in just a couple of minutes. Can you tell what it is?

SOLUTION ON PAGE 184

THE ESCAPE
Part Two

I EXIT FROM THE FAUX BEDROOM that my captors had placed me in to find myself in a large open space, dimly lit. I glance at the door I have just walked through, and realize that it has a note affixed to the outer side as well. I close the door, and study the new note closely.

It seems that this peculiar trial is not yet over. Very well. The first step is to take stock of this odd new space.

My first impression is that I am in a sprawling attic. The ceiling above my head is flat rather than canted, but there is something about the space that makes it feel like an attic. Perhaps it is just the lack of dividing walls. It matters not, really.

The room in which I was originally confined is in one corner of this new space. A pair of relatively thin curtain walls give it the illusion of being a regular room, but from the outside, it is more like a partitioned office. The fake window is set into one of the walls common to both larger and smaller space, but there are not even any false windows in this possible attic. Light is provided by a pair of electric bulbs hanging from the ceiling. The walls seem to be wallpaper over plaster, the floor polished wood like that of the not-bedroom, and the ceiling whitewashed plaster. It is all fairly regular.

There are several installations set around the walls of the room, which I resolve to investigate in a moment. Before I do so, there is the matter of the room's exit. The doorway is the single point of egress from the room, at least assuming that there are no hidden doorways, hatches or ducts. It does not have a door. Instead, a heavy-looking grill of iron bars covers the space, looking uncomfortably like a prison door. This unhappy device extends a good foot past each edge of the door frame, apart from the bottom, where it is flush to the floor. The vertical bars are an inch thick, and held firm with three horizontal pieces of similar size. The whole is welded together. At each side, a thick hasp on the side of the grill fits over a metal tongue protruding from the wall, and a heavy padlock is used to secure it in place.

To The Great Houdini,

I shudder at the thought of gauchely offering congratulations for extricating yourself from such a trifling situation, sir. I am confident that my best efforts hampered you but little, being that I am of such small talent, particularly in matters in which those such as yourself are so astonishingly well versed.

I have attempted, with the space in which you now find yourself, to offer a slightly more varied challenge for your amusement. I doubt you will be delayed so much as to even need to break step, but I can only do my humble best to provide some little entertainment.

As before, I am quite sure that you will find it no difficult matter to exit this room using techniques that involve the minimum of destruction.

Sincerely yours,

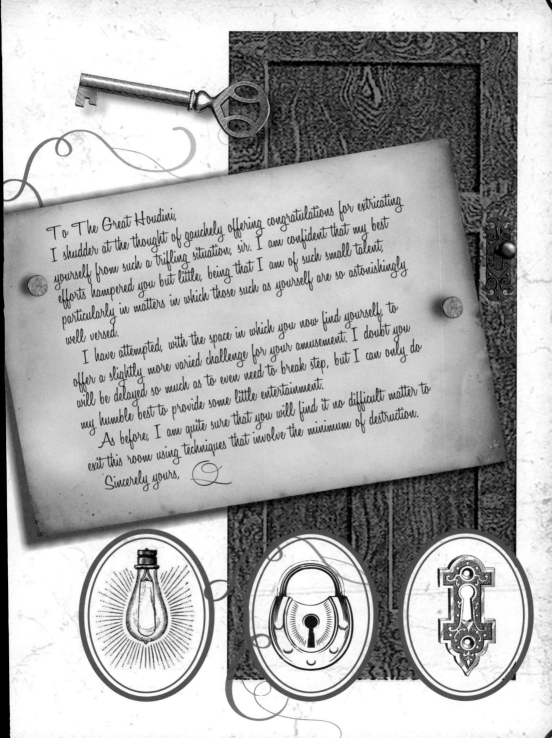

The padlocks appear to be of a custom design, with an unusually thin opening for a key, and no visible screw-heads. Without a look at their works, picking the locks will be ... trying. I have an investigative tug at one, but it seems firm. Both would need to come off to allow removal of the grill. Hmm. Next, I give the bars a rattle. They're as heavy as they look, and sturdily attached, with very little play. Inspecting them more closely, they do not appear to be gimmicked in any way I can ascertain.

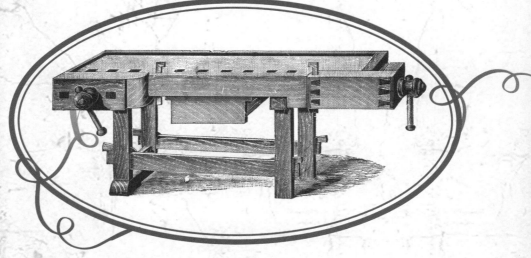

So to the rest of the room. The nearest installation to the door is a hefty wooden workbench, scarred with years of use. It holds a number of woodworking tools, including chisels, a small hammer, nails, a little wood-saw, several steel files, a plane, an adze, and a couple of different shapes of punch. Although well made, none of them are particularly sturdy. The saw, in particular, would cut neither the bars nor the padlock. It might make a dent, but it is clear that it would fail before any useful progress had been made. A pair of heavy vices are built into the front of the desk, big steel things. They are holding about four feet of thick-walled steel pipe, about an inch thick. It could be trivially removed, if I needed to, as the vices are barely even tightened on it. I could possibly disassemble one of the vices as well, and use the front plate for something. Some possibilities here.

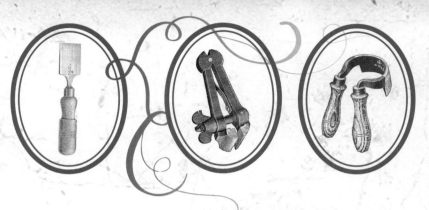

Next is a lighter, longer wooden desk piled with a selection of chemical apparatus. Generally I associate chemistry with glassware, and in that respect I am not disappointed. There are beakers and flasks of various shapes, as well as Petri dishes, glass crucibles, a distiller's alembic, test tubes of all kinds, pipettes and measuring flasks, and things that I have no immediate name for. They all appear empty. A pair of Bunsen burners are connected to small steel taps built into the wall. I turn one of the taps and sniff. It appears to be connected to gas, as one would expect. Interesting. I turn the tap back off. There is also a stash of connective and other supportive materials – small steel tripods with heatproof gauze sheets to support a vessel, pieces of rubber hose, clamps of many types, tongs, droppers, stirrers, wire brushes, and a pestle and mortar. Notably absent are any chemicals, however. Even so, there may well be something useful in here. Taken with the woodworking tools, there is a suggestion of fine work.

The third installation could not be more different in tone or nature. It is nothing less than a three-foot high anvil, to which is chained a heavy-looking smith's hammer. Thick tongs sit on a folded leather apron and gauntlets on the floor beside it. There is a barrel of water next to the anvil, but no forge or bellows. The hammer has about six feet of chain, which is not enough to reach to the door even if I did feel comfortable just smashing the padlocks to bits, which I am not certain I do. There's no way I'm moving the anvil to bring it nearer to the door, either. It is totally immobile.

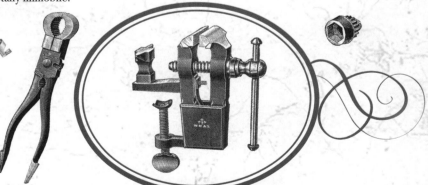

THE ESCAPE
Part Two

On the opposite side of the room from the chemistry bench is an area piled with large wooden packing crates of the sort I tend to associate with commercial shipping. They bear no logos or papers, so they are firmly anonymous. The wood comprising them is relatively flimsy and coarse-grained. Breaking one of them apart would be a very minor act of destruction I feel, and Q's letter did say "a minimum" on this occasion. Anyhow, the crates are not nailed shut, and the tops lift off easily. On a thick bed of straw, each one contains a single primitive artefact – hand axes, arrowheads, and other basic Neolithic tools, most of them crafted from flint or slate by the look of it. Interesting, certainly, but of limited practical usefulness outside the Stone Age. There are 17 crates, and each one seems to hold a good double-armful of straw. Usable? Perhaps.

The final offering in the room is a reading spot. Two bookcases sit behind a comfortable-looking armchair, and there is a small side table next to the chair. A little lamp sits on the table, glowing cheerfully. The bookcases appear to be filled with works of fiction in several different languages – English, French, German and Spanish, at the very least. There are no refreshments set out, but then I still have access to the previous room as well. It would be a very pleasant little nook to devote some time to, but that will not assist in my escape. The cases are wooden, and of standard construction, albeit pleasantly designed and worked. The chair and table seem similarly regular. The seat cushion is not designed to be removed, and feels padded rather than sprung. The lamp finally has a rounded porcelain body, with a small wire-and-cloth shade resting over the light bulb. Its electric cord vanishes into the wall without an obvious plug.

With everything thus examined, I believe I see a relatively straightforward way out. Do you?

SOLUTION ON PAGE 185

The UNDERWATER BOX

Houdini's Underwater Box Escape debuted in 1912, at a performance held on the East River in New York. First, the Great Houdini was firmly handcuffed, and helped into a wooden crate, a cube around four-foot tall made from sturdy planks nailed into place. The lid was placed on top, fastening to the rest of the crate via hasps. These hasps were then padlocked in place over the tongues, and the padlocks chained together.

For good measure, the lid was nailed into place so that even if the padlocks gave, it would still be sealed. A pair of heavy iron pipes were tied to the bottom of the crate, to give it extra weight. Finally, the whole affair was trussed around with ropes, hauled into the air and flung into the river.

Because the crate was punctured on all sides with lots of small holes, it sank into the river very quickly. Two-and-a-half minutes later, Houdini invariably broke the surface. How did he do it?

SOLUTION ON PAGE 186

The MIND READER

AN UNWITTING VOLUNTEER is called from the audience to assist in a demonstration of psychic prowess. After the requisite introductions, she is seated at a small table, across from the Great Houdini. She is presented with a small notepad, and told to write down a number of her choosing and turn the pad over. Whilst she furiously concentrates on the number she has written down, the magician stands, and with his back to the table, reaches behind himself to pick up the pad and tear off the paper.

Now holding the slip of paper behind his back, he enters great paroxysms of concentration, pacing back and forth, eyes narrowed in thought. His hands are kept behind his back, well out of sight. Finally, he has the answer. He shouts out the number, then produces the slip of paper to demonstrate that he was correct.

How does he do it?

SOLUTION ON PAGE 186

BULLET
CATCHER

IN THIS FAMOUS illusion, the magician faces death in the sternest test of physical skill imaginable
– catching a bullet in his teeth. Whilst the Great Houdini stands at one side of the stage,
blindfolded, he explains the ancient provenance of the feat, and the heights of mystical training
required to perform it. Meanwhile, an assistant places a glass drinking tumbler on a stand a few
inches from his mouth, angled so that the base is towards Houdini's face. This, he explains, is
vital to slow the bullet just enough to be able to be caught – but even so, any lesser mortal would
surely find attempting this trick to be a fatal error.

The assistant walks some feet past the open end of the tumbler, produces a pistol, loads it,
and very carefully aims straight at the magician's mouth. With all possible solemnity, Houdini
counts from three to one. A beat later, there's the deafening bang of a gunshot, the glass
shatters, and the magician staggers back, ripping off his blindfold, teeth firmly clamped around
the bullet.

How is this possible?

SOLUTION ON PAGE 186

THE GREAT HOUDINI has concealed 10 differences in the opposite picture. Can you find them?

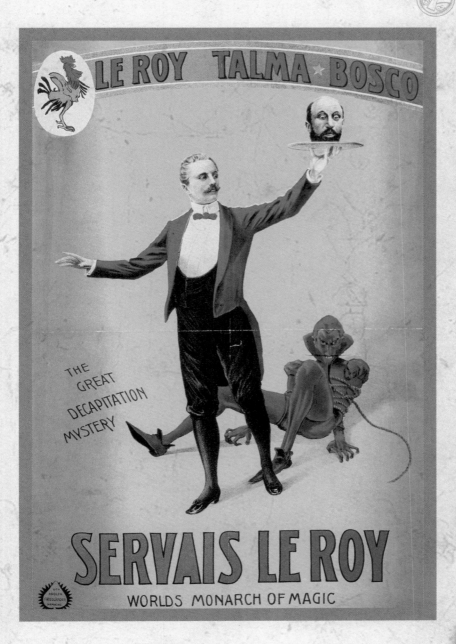

BALANCE

CLOSE YOUR EYES and move your hands around, then hold one still, and touch it with the other. The sense that allows you to do that is the same one that stops you from punching yourself in the face when you scratch your nose. It's called proprioception, and it's vital for balance, which in turn is critical in illusionism and stage magic.

To test out your theoretical understanding of balance, consider this situation. There is a stack of books, several volumes high, sitting neatly at the very edge of a table. Both books and table are perfectly stable, which presumably means the books haven't been opened yet. Perhaps this is in a bookshop. Anyway, it should be obvious that it is possible to pull the top book so it is extending halfway over the edge of the table before it is at risk of falling off the stack.

Perhaps less obviously, you can then pull the second book down part of the way out and still have the first book remain secure. At this point, three quarters of the top-most book – equal to a whole book plus a half book, divided by two – will extend over the edge.

Is it possible to have the top book of the stack completely clear the edge of the table, and if so, how many books do you think you will need?

SOLUTION ON PAGE 188

WISDOM *of* CROWDS

THE MAGICIAN SELECTS a completely innocent member of the audience and brings him up onto the stage for this trick. After the usual preamble and scene-setting, he explains his trick. Whilst the Great Houdini languishes, blindfolded, in a completely opaque wooden box, the volunteer will write a number between 1 and 100 on a large piece of paper, and silently show it to the audience. Then the paper is destroyed by an assistant, and Houdini is brought back from his seclusion.

Then, as the audience all concentrate upon the number, the magician will attempt to read that information from their minds. It is very difficult, picking up clear information from so many different thought patterns, but finally he announces the number – the same one that was written on the paper.

How does he do it?

SOLUTION ON PAGE 188

FLAT OUT

IN THIS ILLUSION, the Great Houdini walks over to a carpeted portion of the stage, and explains that he is going to defy gravity itself – but not by flying. Instead, he carefully lies down, arms and legs together. Then several assistants enter from the wings, pushing between them a huge, heavy turf roller. This massive device has a central roller a foot in diameter and three feet in width, cast as a single lump of solid iron. A pole running through the centre permits it to rotate, and metal sheeting runs back on either side from the central pin. The handle that moves the whole contraption is a good five feet in length, and it takes four men straining to push it across the stage.

They get it moving, however, and advance towards the magician's feet, neatly together in front of them. To the horror of the crowd, they do not slow as the roller lumbers up the stretch of carpet. Within moments, it is at Houdini's feet – and then over them. As the magician groans horribly in clear agony, his oblivious assistants push forwards, crushing him into the planks. It is blatantly clear that the roller is genuine, and in contact with the stage floor. They finally come to a stop at last with the roller over his hips.

A disaster, surely – but the curtain falls, and then Houdini bounds out from behind it, having cheated death again. How?

SOLUTION ON PAGE 189

HOUDINI'S
METAL-
Rimmed BOX

HOUDINI'S METAL-RIMMED Box was a wooden crate much like the ones typically used in packing and shipping. All the edges were held together with square-angled metal running their entire length. Extensive nailing made the construction extremely solid. Members of the public were invited to look at the box, give it a shake, and make sure that it was as it seemed to be.

The trick itself was comparatively simple. Houdini climbed into the box, crouched down, and the lid was placed on and nailed shut. With no air holes anywhere in the woodwork, it would only be a short matter of time before he would suffocate to death if he failed to escape.

The curtain came down, and the audience watched anxiously, listening to the thumps of struggle, before the great magician came forth, free and in fine health.

How did he do it?

SOLUTION ON PAGE 189

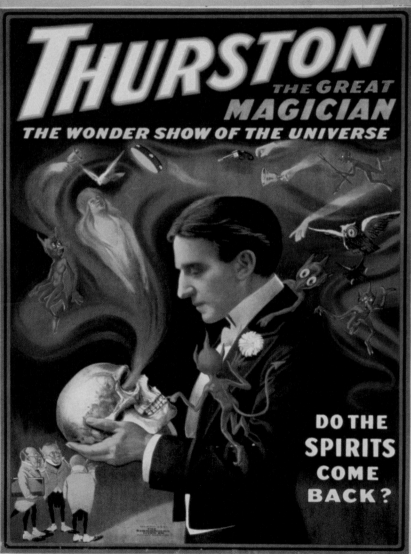

THE GREAT HOUDINI has concealed 10 differences in the opposite picture. Can you find them?

THURSTON
THE GREAT
MAGICIAN
THE WONDER SHOW OF THE UNIVERSE

DO THE
SPIRITS
COME
BACK

SOLUTION ON PAGE 190

WALKING ON WATER

THE GREAT HOUDINI explains to the audience that through his many years of study into the mystic arts of the East, as mentioned before, he has managed to attain a great many powers and abilities unknown to common man. Amongst these is the ability to lighten the molecular structure of his body until he weighs little more than a feather. To prove this, he will walk on water itself.

A large tank of water is pushed on to the stage, glass-sided throughout. It's about a foot high, two or three feet wide, and maybe ten feet long. The magician walks around it, reaching down to splash the water repeatedly so that everyone can see that it is indeed perfectly normal water.

A step is put next to the edge of the tank, the same height. Houdini mounts this, and prepares himself, entering a deep trance. Then he calmly takes a step forward, onto the water – and he does not sink. He takes another step, and another, and everyone in the crowd can see that there is nothing but water in the tank.

With no wires to support his weight, how can Houdini manage this feat?

SOLUTION ON PAGE 191

LEVITATION

IN THIS PUBLIC trick, the Great Houdini rides around the city on a perfectly regular bus – but not in a seat. Instead, he casually holds on to the outside of the bus with his left hand, and hangs in the air in perfect comfort, supporting his entire weight on that one hand. Indeed, he hovers around the city for an hour or more, waving pleasantly at shocked onlookers and baffled passengers.

But how?

SOLUTION ON PAGE 191

ESCAPE

THE MAZE

START

END

SOLUTION ON PAGE 192

PATTERN RECOGNITION

PATTERNS ARE A crucial tool in the illusionist's armoury. Established, they will lead human perception and behaviour down predictable paths, and predictability is always a point of weakness.

As an example, consider the matter of a guard on a simple patrol route. Once you observe the patterns of his movement, you know precisely how much time you have between his appearances. That is a weakness in the security his presence attempts to establish.

This can be made slightly more secure by having the guard randomly choose which direction to make his circuit, clockwise or anticlockwise, just before he sets off. Suddenly, precise matters of timing are a lot more difficult. Even so, there is a pattern, and a weakness associated with it. The guard will be at the same location at the same moment once in every patrol, whichever way he sets off.

Can you see why?

SOLUTION ON PAGE 192

JEWELLERY

THE GREAT HOUDINI stands in front of a long glass jewellery case, the solid panes of glass mounted in a wooden frame. Inside are a dazzling selection of treasures – diamond necklaces, beautifully worked rings, antique gold watches, glittering gemstones, and much more besides. He raps upon the surface in several places to show that it is solid. After explaining that the items are on loan from a local museum for the purposes of his feat, he indicates a few of the items sealed inside the case, pointing them out with one hand whilst the other rests on one of the jeweller's cloths that are positioned at either end of the case. The magician goes into loving detail about the fascinating provenance of the items he indicates, which have all carved a bright trail down through history.

Then, Houdini explains that he is going to make use of his special powers to plunge his hand through the glass without breaking it. This will allow him to retrieve a prize item from inside the case, which will remain completely sealed the entire time. He brings his hands together over a particularly fine diamond necklace. Suddenly he reaches through the pane and swiftly flips out the necklace, then steps back with a flourish. The diamond necklace is in his grasp, and the case remains undamaged.

How?

SOLUTION ON PAGE 193

HOUDINI'S IRON BOX CHALLENGE

FOR THIS TRICK, Houdini made use of a solid iron trunk, riveted together at all sides, with air holes and larger visibility holes, so that it was clear that he was actually inside. The box had an iron cover that was completely separate, a heavy lid with four hasps which also had air and visibility holes. These were fastened by large bolts that were screwed in place through holes in the sides, with the nuts firmly securing the hasps in place. The bolts had holes through them near the end, where padlocks could be threaded to ensure that there was no way the bolt could be retracted.

Once everyone had inspected the box to their contentment, Houdini was sealed into it, and the locks put in place. Then the magician was screened. Some minutes later, he would emerge, and when the screen was taken away, the box was there still intact and firmly locked.

How did he do it?

SOLUTION ON PAGE 193

PUZZLE CHAIN

FIRST LINK

The Great Houdini is caught in another, longer, chain of puzzles. To save him, you will have to work your way through the chain, making careful note of your answers to each link. You'll need them all if you're going to successfully open the cunning puzzle lock that binds him. For the greatest challenge, do not check to see if your answers are correct until after you've completed the final lock.

How much should the right-most weight weigh to ensure that the beam balances? That number is the value of the first link in the chain.

SOLUTION ON PAGE 194

PUZZLE CHAIN

$$9 \quad 4 \quad 5 \quad (X) \quad 3 \quad 10 \quad 2 \quad 4 = 24$$

In the calculation above, all the operands have been removed. X is equal to the value of the first link. Replace the missing operands, using at least one each of +, −, x, and /, and no others, so that the calculation is correct. When figuring out the answer, ignore usual mathematical priority, and perform each calculation strictly in the order it appears on the page.

Can you do it?

The number of "+" signs in the final calculation is the value of the second link in the chain.

SOLUTION ON PAGE 194

PUZZLE CHAIN

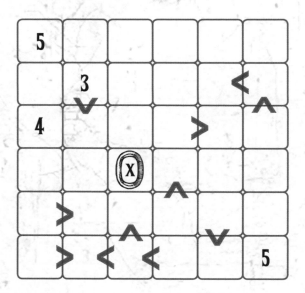

Each row and column of this grid contains the numbers 1–6 once exactly. The chevrons (">" signs) between cells indicate that the number on the wide side of the chevron is larger than the number on the pointed side. In the grid, the letter X represents the value of the second link in the chain. The value of the third link in the chain is equal to the number in the top-right square of the completed grid.

What is it?

SOLUTION ON PAGE 194

FOURTH LINK

PUZZLE CHAIN

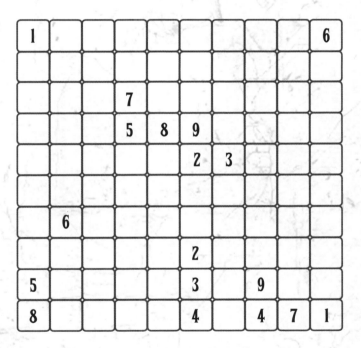

Each number in the grid above is connected to its identical partner by an unbroken line of cells. These lines never bunch to form a two-by-two (or larger) square. When the grid is filled correctly, every square is used. The value of the third link will give you the number of extra squares needed to correctly connect the two fours.

The value of the fourth link is equal to the number of squares in the line connecting the two nines, including the start and end square. What is it?

SOLUTION ON PAGE 195

PUZZLE CHAIN

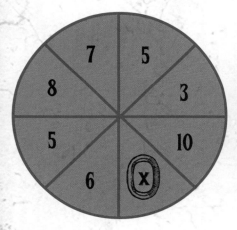
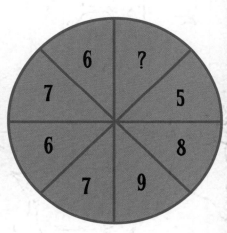

The values in the circles follow a certain specific logic. The X represents the value of the fourth link. The number that should correctly replace the question mark is equal to the value of the fifth link. What it is?

SIXTH LINK

PUZZLE CHAIN

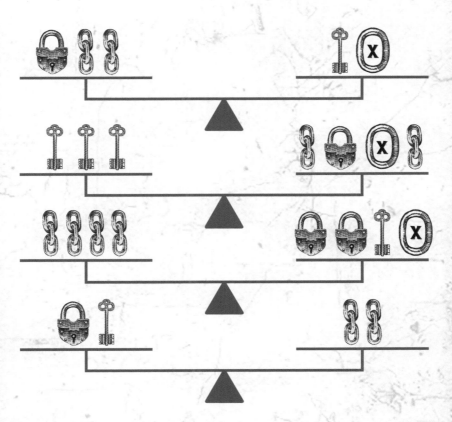

These scales are set up so that they balance, with the sum of the values of each tray equalling its partner. X represents the value of the fifth link. The value of the symbol that appears twice on the right-hand tray of the bottom scale is equal to the value of the sixth link. What is it?

SOLUTION ON PAGE 195

PUZZLE CHAIN

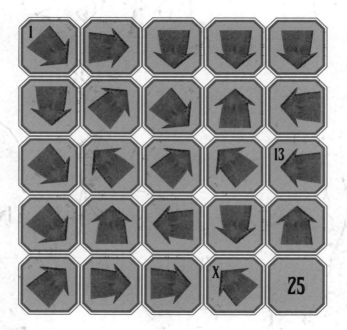

The aim of this numeric maze is to work your way from square 1 to square 25, stopping exactly once at each other square on the way. You can move any distance from the square you are on, but only in the precise direction indicated by the arrow.

Number the squares in the sequence you land on them, starting from square 1. The X is equal to the value of the sixth link in the chain, and tells you the correct sequence number of the square it occupies.

There is only one correct route. When you have it, check the sequence number of the bottom-left square. This number is the value of the seventh link in the chain. What is it?

SOLUTION ON PAGE 196

PUZZLE CHAIN

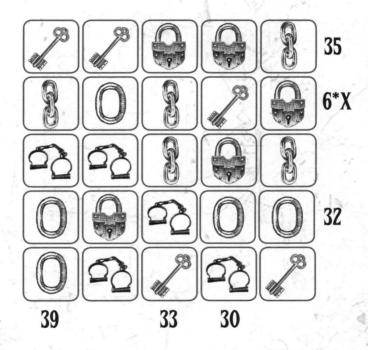

In this grid, each symbol has a consistent value, and the sums of the values of the symbols in certain rows and columns are given at the end of that line of symbols. X is equal to the value of the seventh link in the chain. Knowing this, what is the value of the symbol in the top right? The answer to this gives you the value of the eighth link in the chain.

SOLUTION ON PAGE 196

PUZZLE
CHAIN

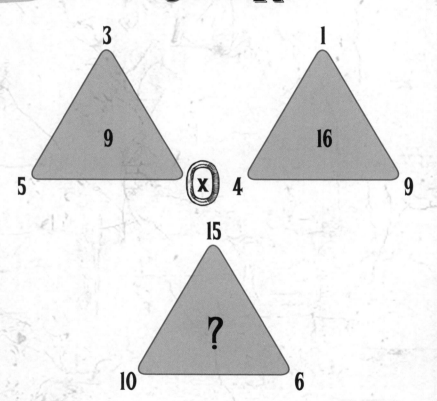

These triangles follow a certain consistent logic. X is equal to the value of the eighth link. What number should replace the question mark?

SOLUTION ON PAGE 197

PUZZLE
CHAIN

		h	i		5	2		
	3						6	
6		9				5		a
5				e				6
			6		1			
8				5				2
f		1				8		b
	9						1	
		d	c		2	g		

To finally unlock the chain binding the Great Houdini, you have to complete this grid of numbers correctly. In it, each row, column, and highlighted block of 3x3 cells contains the numbers 1–9 exactly once.

The letters a to i in the grid represent the values of the first through to the ninth links respectively, so C = the third link, and G = the seventh link.

Can you complete the grid and free Houdini?

SOLUTION ON PAGE 197

93

COMBINATOR

IT IS VITALLY important that any illusionist should have a firm grasp of at least the basics of probability theory. Some tricks rely on a little luck to work smoothly, and you need to have a good idea of what to do if it doesn't fall your way. An understanding of how likely that is will help immensely in putting together any act.

Picture a lock with a row of numeric dials rather than a key. They are in fact quite insecure in general, but they do look daunting. This one has six dials, each numbered 0 to 9. You know that one of the dials needs to be set to 5, but not which. What is your chance of guessing the correct answer on your first try?

SOLUTION ON PAGE 197

HOUDINI'S PLATE-GLASS BOX

THE PLATE-GLASS Box was, as its name suggests, a large crate made from sheets of plate glass, held together with steel banding along all the edges. The steel is bolted together through holes cut in the glass plates. This design allowed Houdini to remain fully visible whilst inside, although his actual escape from it was of course performed behind a curtain or screen. This was one of the escapes that his wife Bess, his on-stage assistant, also performed sometimes.

The lid is actually a permanent part of this box, which was often not the case in Houdini's boxes. It is hinged, and locked in place by hasps which are padlocked over tongues protruding from the top steel edge.

For the performance, Houdini was typically handcuffed then chained and shackled, and locked into the box. After he'd been suitably examined, a curtain came across, and shortly he'd be out, the box still fastened together every bit as firmly as before.

How did he do it?

SOLUTION ON PAGE 198

SPIDER-MAN

THE GREAT HOUDINI announces a spectacle in a public location. At the appointed time, a spotlight appears, and swings around to pick him out of the evening sky. He is standing on the roof of a tall building overlooking the area. He's very high up, but he seems blithely unconcerned that he's standing on the edge of a fatal drop.

There is no harness anywhere in sight, no safety ropes, not even a gantry from which such a thing could be hung. Nevertheless, in defiance of gravity itself, he leans further and further over the edge, until he is at an impossible angle. But he keeps going, and suddenly he is fully horizontal. The magician then starts comfortably walking down the side of the building, as fully at ease as if he were just taking a stroll. When he reaches the ground, he tilts himself up a bit, steps forward so that he's upright, and takes a bow.

How is this possible?

SOLUTION ON PAGE 198

DISPLACEMENT

AS MENTIONED EARLIER, if you are going to perform illusions involving water, it's vitally important to know exactly how water is going to behave. There is no room for error when you're sealed in a water-filled box, even if the box is less secure than it looks.

So picture a pair of identical buckets, exactly full to the brim with water. The one on the left holds nothing extra, but the one on the right has a large piece of wood floating on the surface of the water.

Which of the buckets is heavier?

SOLUTION ON PAGE 198

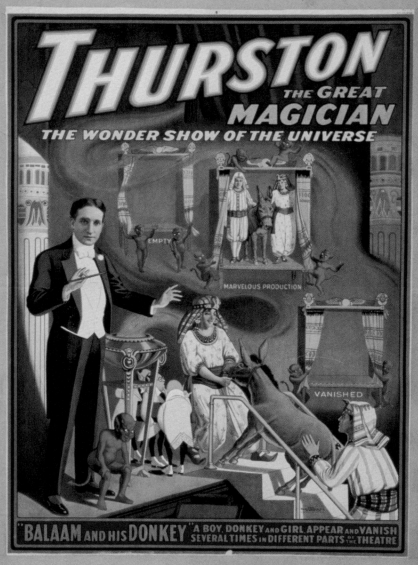

THE GREAT HOUDINI has concealed 10 differences in the opposite picture. Can you find them?

SOLUTION ON PAGE 199

HOUDINI'S SPANISH MAIDEN ESCAPE

IN THIS DISTURBING escape, Houdini had himself locked inside an Iron Maiden, a famous device used for torture during medieval times. It takes the form of a metal box shaped to approximate the human form. The inside of the box is lined with evil-looking spikes, both at the back and on the front. Houdini's device, which he called his "Spanish Maiden", stood upright, and often had a painting of a young Hispanic woman on the front.

The audience was assured that the spikes were placed so as to not cut Houdini to ribbons. Even so, there was no spare room, and movement was nearly impossible without injuring himself gravely. Once he was inside, the hinged lid was swung shut and fastened in place with hasps fitted over tongues that held it to the main body and then padlocked in place. Observers were allowed to examine the device, and ensure for themselves that from the inside, there was no way that the magician could get to the padlocks.

How did Houdini escape?

SOLUTION ON PAGE 200

THE SWITCH

IN THIS ILLUSION, the Great Houdini is firmly bound and tied by his assistant, and led to a platform, where a sheet is thrown over him. The platform then slowly rises into the air, lifted by a hoist. Meanwhile, his assistant takes a place on the stage, near where the platform departed from. She lifts a sheet up in front of herself, then drops it as the cymbals clash, to reveal the magician himself, there on the stage. In the same instant, the figure on the platform throws that sheet off, to show that it is the assistant, somehow bound and tied in Houdini's place.

How did they manage it?

SOLUTION ON PAGE 200

START

END

SOLUTION ON PAGE 201

AN ILLUSION
of MAGICIANS

A GROUP OF six professional magicians, known to one another but not entirely friendly with each other, entirely fill one compartment of a train carriage. They sit in two rows of three, facing each other. Certain items of information are provided below.

The six men are called Robert, Anderson, Hermann, Devant, Blackstone and Maskelyne. Between them, their specialities cover playing cards, rope tricks, coins, escapology, mentalism, and feats of daring, and each is studying a report of a recent trick performed by one of the others in the carriage. No two reports are about the same person.

Hermann is reading about a performance given by the person sitting opposite him. Robert, who does not specialize in ropes, is reading about a card trick. Anderson, not the escapologist, is sitting between the coin specialist and the card-trick performer, who, in turn, is opposite the rope specialist. Devant is reading about mentalism and sitting opposite the escapologist. Blackstone, reading about a coin trick, is next to the mentalist. Robert is sitting in a corner. Maskelyne, finally, is not studying a feat of daring.

Who is the escapologist?

SOLUTION ON PAGE 201

DOING
the TWIST

IN A SWIFT but stunning feat, the Great Houdini calls an innocent audience member on to the stage, and talks with them for a moment. He is standing next to a table, with one hand resting on it. Then he lifts up his hand, staggers a few steps from the table, and slowly begins to turn it. Groaning horribly, his face twisted with pain, he continues twisting until his hand has rotated in a complete circle, a full 360 degrees. He then apologizes as if having inconvenienced the audience member, and continues with his next trick.

How does he do this? It's certainly not because he is double-jointed.

SOLUTION ON PAGE 202

HOUDINI'S EAST INDIAN NEEDLE TRICK

FOR THIS TRICK, Houdini invited a genuine audience member up on to the stage to carefully examine some objects for him – a large bundle of fine needles, up to 100 of them, and some sixty feet of common sewing thread. Once the spectator was happy that these things were genuine, the magician used his fingers to hook his mouth open, so that the person could carefully check under his tongue and behind his teeth.

With the formalities out of the way, Houdini had his assistant gather up the needles and thread, and bring them to him with a glass of water. He then put them into his mouth, and swallowed them down with a swig from the glass. A few moments later, after some extremely uncomfortable-looking contortions, the magician opened his mouth and pulled out the needles – threaded securely in place along the entire length of the yarn.

How?

SOLUTION ON PAGE 202

THURSTON
WORLD'S FAMOUS MAGICIAN
THE WONDER SHOW OF THE UNIVERSE

THE GREAT HOUDINI has concealed 10 differences in the opposite picture. Can you find them?

SOLUTION ON PAGE 203

THE
CIGARETTE

BRANDISHING A LIT cigarette, the Great Houdini tells the audience the common lie about the temperature of the burning part of the cigarette exceeding the temperature of the surface of the sun (in reality, it's about 5,000 degrees lower). To prove his point, he declares that he is going to melt right through a coin. An audience member is called to the stage to examine the coin and pronounce it normal.

Once that is taken care of, the magician takes several puffs on the cigarette to get it nice and hot – and stabs it right through the centre of the coin he is brandishing. He even holds up the cigarette with the coin balanced on it, to show that it has melted its way through.

How is this done?

SOLUTION ON PAGE 204

MALLEABLE

THE GREAT HOUDINI asks the audience if someone is prepared to lend him a quarter, or another local coin of fairly small denomination. An innocent volunteer is selected more or less at random, and brought up to the stage. After the usual introductions, the volunteer hands over a quarter. The magician explains that he is going to use his incredible mastery of mind over matter to make the coin softer than it normally should be.

So saying, he brings the coin up to his mouth, and bites a chunk out of it! He shows the bitten coin around, so that everyone can see a piece is indeed missing. But he reassures them that he will repair it again. Bringing the coin to his mouth a second time, he spits the missing piece back into place, and suddenly it is whole again. After taking a bow, he gives the coin back to the spectator, who examines it with amazement.

How is it done?

◄ SOLUTION ON PAGE 204 ►

THE ESCAPE
Part Three

WITH THE BARS tucked safely out of the way, I walk down a short stretch of passageway and come to a flight of stairs. They seem to stretch on, but finally I come to the bottom, where there is a door. My curious captor has left another note on it, pinned in place.

Last stage, huh? That sounds promising, at least. I push open the door, and find myself in a short stretch of perfectly regular hallway of the sort that might be found in any home. Several doors lead off the hallway, some made of solid wood and presumably interior, and one with glass panes inset, looking out on a porch and attractive front garden. Beyond the garden is a road, and the world! I try the door, but it is locked. I expected nothing less, but it was worth making sure. The lock is quite large and fairly old-fashioned, made of sturdy-looking ironwork. I look around for a key, but naturally there is none to be seen.

Instead, the hallway offers a small side table bearing a pottery bowl. Several apples and pears sit in the bowl. I doubt Q would mind if I took one, given the refreshments upstairs, but I am fine for the moment. A watercolour painting of an Italian-looking villa on a hillside sits above the bowl. Opposite, there is an empty row of wooden coat hangers. The walls are papered with a striped design, perfectly pleasant if not especially exciting, and the floor of the hall is a chequered pattern of six-inch-square tiles, of cream and dark blue. There's a light fixture in the ceiling, a three-bulbed affair with simple lampshades, and a switch on the wall, near the front door. A bristle mat sits just inside the door. I lift it just to make absolutely certain that the key isn't underneath. It isn't.

Apart from the front door and the door up to the space which encloses me, there are three other doors off the entrance hall, one to the left, one to the right, and one at the end of the hall.

I decide to go through the end door first, and find myself in a large kitchen. The main light is on, and it's immediately obvious why – the windows, which are large and plentiful, have been bricked up from outside. If there was any doubt that Q had gone to substantial inconvenience in preparing the environment, it is surely now laid to rest. A thought nags at the back of my

To The Great Houdini,

By this point, sir, you have undoubtedly perceived the very limited extent of my imagination. I confess that my mind did turn at first to hidden panels and gimmicked bolts, but in the absence of extra information to clue you in to the same, they seem an unreasonably stern contrivance.

There is one final barrier to your freedom, flimsy as it will most certainly prove. I hope with the greatest sincerity that you have derived some minor degree of diversion from my paltry efforts — my little attempt to repay the great pleasure your work has often provided to myself and my friends.

I remain grateful, during this last stage, for your kind and gracious forbearance in restraining from physical damage to my humble abode and its trifling contents.

Sincerely yours,

THE ESCAPE
Part Three

mind, but it is gone before I can pin it down. The kitchen is tidy and well appointed, floored with glazed terracotta tiles in a mock-rustic fashion. The walls have the same paper as the hallway. A vast, heavy cast-iron oven and stove dominates one entire wall of the room. It is enamelled in a cream colour, and boasts four separate oven compartments and six burners along the top. Although it does not appear to be in use, it is quite warm. A formidable piece of cooking equipment, to be sure.

There are three large ceramic sinks beneath the bricked-up windows, each with a faucet and plughole, complete with rubber plug. I try one of the faucets and, sure enough, the water is connected. A Welsh dresser stands against one of the walls, boasting an entire dinner service of attractively decorated china, and a drawer holds an equally extensive range of cutlery, even down to crab-crackers. The main work surface is a large, heavy wooden table. A dozen pots and skillets of assorted sizes, all cast in iron, hang above it from a sturdy row of hooks. A block of cooking and carving knives rests at one end of the table. A small slatted wooden door leads into a pantry with space for several weeks of provisions. At the moment, it just holds some staples

– flour, sugar, tins of fruit and vegetables, and the like. I suppose I could sift through the flour and sugar to make sure nothing is hidden therein, and I resolve to give it a try if all else fails. The generous refrigerator next to the Welsh dresser is similarly depleted, with milk, eggs and butter, but little else. I could make a fruit pie, but I'm not really in the mood for cookery. None of the ingredients seems unusual in any way.

A second door leads from the kitchen into a large dining room. The light is on in here too, and behind heavy floor-length curtains are more bricked-up windows. The brickwork does not look particularly solid, but it would definitely be destructive to smash my way out, and at this point, that somehow feels like losing. Apparently, I have become accustomed to treating this as a game. The dining-room floor is covered in a thick deep-green carpet which works quite harmoniously with the ever-present wallpaper. The furnishings and fittings are all of wood, probably mahogany. They include a service station piled high with cloths and bearing several carafes, a large dining table with ten chairs set around it, and a drinks cabinet similar to the one I found next to my bedside when I awoke. Several more watercolours are on the walls, by the same artist I think. A slightly darker patch of wallpaper shows where (presumably) a clock has been removed. Interesting. Another door leads back into the hallway.

One final door remains. I go through and find myself in an attractive sitting room of similar size to the dining room. As before, the light is turned on, and the several windows have been bricked up, their curtains tied back. The room holds two couches, one chaise, four separate armchairs, a couple of dining chairs and two coffee tables. The focus of the room is a large fireplace, currently empty. A stand next to the grate holds an ash-pan, brush, and selection of pokers. The back of the chimney is quite wide, but when I investigate it, the flue narrows quickly. I can find nothing hidden there.

One of the coffee tables bears several books – three recently released novels, and a more serious volume on nineteenth-century German history – along with a glass vase of chrysanthemums, and a partly completed knitting project, which includes a ball of yarn with a pair of sturdy needles threaded through it.

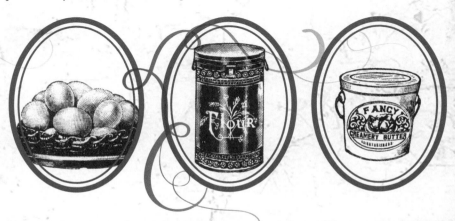

THE ESCAPE
Part Three

The other coffee table holds an empty mug, a copy of *Harper's*, a small hand-mirror, and a hairbrush, hairpin and pair of interesting jade combs. Clearly, Q has gone to efforts to give this room the appearance of a natural environment, but I find myself doubting everything. I move the knitting, the mug and anything else that might conceal some useful tool, but find nothing. As in the other rooms, the walls are covered with the same wallpaper, and there are several more of the watercolours. On the floor is the same carpet as in the dining room, but it is almost entirely covered with an expensive Persian rug of intricate design.

A door is ajar at the far side of the living room. Through it, I find a small but tidy office. This has a desk of similar aesthetic to the writing desk in the room I was first in, with a forest-green leatherwork area set in mahogany, and a wing-backed chair with matching seat. There is nothing on the desk, however, and it has no drawers. Three glass-fronted bookcases sit opposite the desk. The shelves are packed with files and volumes that could be diaries or ledgers, but the cases are locked. Clearly I am not supposed to pry. Some indents in the green carpet near one of the walls suggest strongly to me that this is the usual home of the writing desk and drinks cabinet I woke up near to. Some darker squares and rectangles on the wallpaper imply that some items have been removed as too revealing, but a pair of the watercolours remain, studies of the same gnarled olive tree, but from different angles.

That appears to be all that the area I can access has to offer. I strongly suspect that there is more of the house hidden away behind a section of wallpapered panel, but it doesn't actually matter. I have what I need to leave this place.

Can you see how?

SOLUTION ON PAGE 204

BEATING
the ODDS

WEIGHTED COINS AND loaded dice are staples of the trade for both gamblers and illusionists. They're made by changing the distribution of mass so that one side is heavier than the other, and thus there's a bigger chance of the opposite side coming up. They don't work every time – a coin or die unbalanced enough to give a 100 per cent result is immediately obvious to anyone who holds it – but in the long run, they can give a strong advantage.

If you suspect you are facing a weighted coin in a matter of supposed chance, it is possible to defeat the weighting, and get a genuinely fair result from tossing it.

Can you see how?

SOLUTION ON PAGE 205

HOUDINI'S WALL PASSAGE

THIS TRICK INVOLVED a brick wall, nine feet high and ten feet wide, which was built across the stage, brick by brick, as Houdini performed other feats and illusions. This allowed the audience to see that the wall was genuinely solid. It was positioned side-on to the audience, so that they could see both sides, and built on a large piece of carpet, so that the magician couldn't enter any trapdoors. Once it was completed, audience members were called up on to the stage to feel the wall, push at it, even hammer on it, so that they could be confident that it was solid throughout. The wall stretched back to the rear of the stage, so there was no way to go around it without being in full view.

When everything was ready, and the audience reseated, Houdini took his position on one side of the wall. Screens were wheeled in, one in front of him, and one on a similar position but on the other side of the wall. Just seconds after they were put in place, they were pulled away again, to reveal Houdini on the far side of the wall. Throughout this time, the audience had full view of the wall itself, so knew for sure that he hadn't scaled it or darted in front of it.

How did he do it?

SOLUTION ON PAGE 205

THE FLY

THIS TRICK IS not typically performed on a stage, but in more intimate surroundings. The Great Houdini reveals to a group of awed onlookers that he is going to perform the miracle of resurrection itself. He looks around, and spots a dead fly, in a corner or on a windowsill. He encourages the people around him to poke at it. It is utterly unresponsive.

The magician picks the dead insect up, and lays it on the palm of his hand. Then he concentrates, focussing his power. Soon, to the amazement of the onlookers, the fly begins to move. In just a matter of minutes, it is back fully alive, and buzzes off.

How is this possible?

SOLUTION ON PAGE 205

THREE CUPS

LATERAL THINKING IS a vital part of the magician's stagecraft. Typically it is most used in figuring out how to put tricks together – no trick can survive being obvious – but sometimes it's also used overtly, to gently show the audience how their patterns of thought might blind them to possibilities. Few stage shows do well when flat-out mocking the audience at large, of course, so be circumspect.

For this exercise, picture ten coins and three regular paper cups. Can you place all the coins into the cups so that each cup contains an odd number of coins?

SOLUTION ON PAGE 206

ESCAPE THE MAZE

EXIT

SOLUTION ON PAGE 206

FRUITY

THE GREAT HOUDINI calls an innocent member of the audience up on to the stage to assist with a demonstration of his mental powers. After introductions, he picks up a deck of cards, fans through it quickly to show that it is regular, and then squares it off. He then asks the spectator to think of a card, without telling him which. Once she has one, he tells her to look for it carefully as he fans through the deck again, which he does more slowly this time. Incredibly, the card isn't in there.

The spectator tells the magician which card she picked, and he reveals that in fact he already used her mental focus to identify the card and teleport it out. He crosses to a bowl of fruit, and selects a piece. Then he returns with a knife, slices the fruit open, and pulls a rolled-up card from inside of it. The card is the one she chose.

How does he do it?

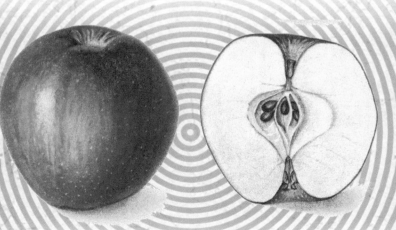

SOLUTION ON PAGE 207

LACED

~·—••◦•◦•—••·~

THIS IS A quick but often impressive trick, one typically used when up close with a group of people. The Great Houdini looks down and sees that his shoelace has come untied. After pointing this fact out to the people around him and apologizing for this shocking breach of dress code, he lifts his foot and shakes it vigorously. When he lowers it again, his shoelace is tied in a perfect bow.

How is this possible?

SOLUTION ON PAGE 207

GOING WRONG

FOR THIS COMPLEX card trick, the Great Houdini enlists an innocent member of the audience. When the volunteer is up on stage and fully introduced, Houdini fans a deck of cards and asks her to select one, and show it openly to everyone. Then she inserts it back into the deck. The magician then pretends to attempt to use his mind power to force the card to the top of the deck without touching it, but when he whips off the top card to display it, it's the wrong card. He slaps it back down, then, infuriated, grabs it again and rips it up, then gives it to his volunteer to hold tightly.

Then he picks up the next card from the deck – but it's the same wrong one he just tore. He tells her to look at the torn card, and it's the card she chose! Well, this is just no good at all. It's not supposed to be that card that's torn. He takes it, shows the two halves around irritably, then hands it back to her, pressing it back into her hand. Then he puts his hands over hers and concentrates. When she looks at her card, it's just folded up. The tear is gone.

How?

SOLUTION ON PAGE 208

ON *the* RADIO

THE GREAT HOUDINI announces that he is going to make a perfectly ordinary radio vanish, converting it into the same electromagnetic energy it receives. His assistant brings in the radio on a silver tray. To show that it's the real deal, Houdini turns it on and tunes it to a local radio station for a snatch of music.

Once the radio's reality has been established, the magician throws a piece of cloth over the radio set. Then he takes hold of the radio through the cloth, holding it by the top. The assistant whisks the plate away and leaves, allowing the magician to be the focus of attention with his radio.

With a flourish, he whips the cloth in the air – the radio is gone.

How?

SOLUTION ON PAGE 208

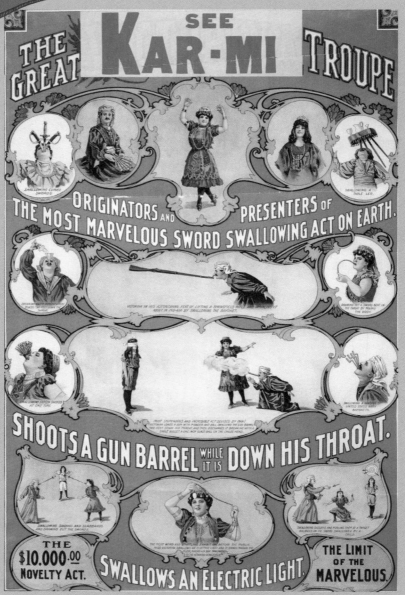

THE GREAT HOUDINI has concealed 10 differences in the opposite picture. Can you find them?

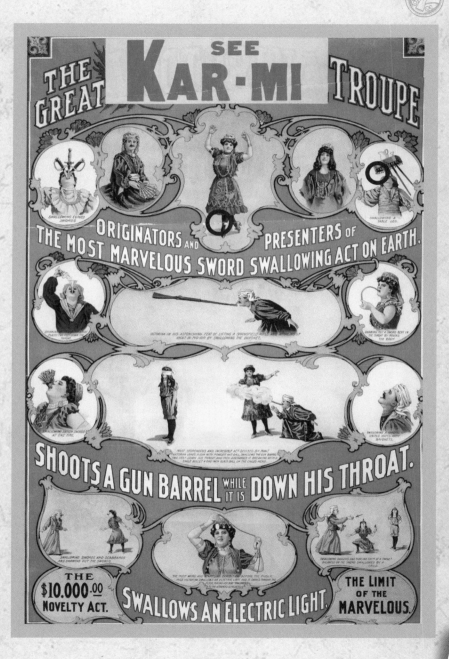

CHAINS
of LOGIC

How ARE YOUR abilities of logical inference and deduction? Consider the following statements, and assume that they are true:

- The facts that make up this trick are not presented in sequential order.
- If I read about a trick without muttering, that is because it is not confusing.
- I only mutter when reading about tricks if my teeth itch.
- This collection of seven facts constitutes a trick.
- If the facts of a trick are not sequential, I do not understand them.
- A trick I do not understand makes my teeth itch.
- Confusing tricks are ones which I do not understand.

Does reading about this trick make my teeth itch?

SOLUTION ON PAGE 210

HOUDINI'S METAMORPHOSIS

IN THIS GROUNDBREAKING illusion, Houdini had his hands tied behind his back, and he was then helped into a large canvas bag. The bag was knotted closed with a rope that ran through ringlet holes around the top, and lifted into a large box. This was in turn locked and strapped up, and placed inside a curtain-fronted screening cabinet. Houdini's assistant – his wife, Bessie – then pulled a curtain in front of the cabinet, and clapped three times. At the third clap, the curtain fell away to reveal Harry Houdini standing there. He would then remove the cabinet, unlock the box, unfasten the bag, and reveal Bess kneeling where he should have been, her hands tied behind her back as his were.

How?

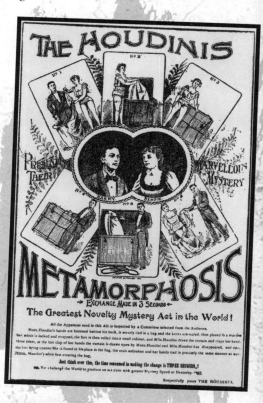

SOLUTION ON PAGE 210

EXIT

SOLUTION ON PAGE 211

The SPINNING ASSISTANT

IN THIS TRICK, the Great Houdini mounts a small pedestal to show off a tall cabinet connected to a hinge on one side. It has a door on the front, with small viewing panels at top and bottom. He explains that the cabinet can be rotated to be upside down, and then pushes it in the direction of the hinge. Slowly, it turns until it has completely rotated 180 degrees around the hinge. Then he opens the door, and shows that the inside is extremely shallow and very narrow.

The magician helps his slender assistant into the cabinet, then closes and locks the door, trapping her in place. He opens the view-holes at top and bottom to show her face and ankles, then closes them again. Then, after a few words of encouragement to her, he slowly rotates the cabinet again. But when he opens the top view-hole, instead of her ankles, there's her face, still right side up. He unlocks the door, and out she strolls.

Why isn't she upside down?

SOLUTION ON PAGE 211

FLOATING FOOD

THE GREAT HOUDINI picks up a can of tinned vegetables, of the sort you would find on the shelves of any grocery store. Explaining how his mastery over gravity has given him unusual powers, he holds the can lightly in his hands, supporting it with his fingertips to either side. This allows him to show the can off to the audience. Then he concentrates, and slowly moves his fingertips away.

Incredibly, the can does not fall. It just hovers there, in front of his spread hands.

How?

SOLUTION ON PAGE 212

The
DIVIDED GIRL

ONE OF THE MOST famous of all magic tricks, this requires the help of the magician's assistant. The Great Houdini presents a tall cabinet with three lockable portholes and a pair of slits in the door. He opens it to show that it is perfectly regular, and then helps his assistant into it. He closes the door, and opens the portholes to show her face, her left hand, and her feet.

The portholes are closed up again, and the magician picks up a pair of wide sharp blades. He puts these into the slits in turn, wiggling them to force them through his unfortunate assistant, and finally slamming them into place, chopping her into sections. Then he pushes the middle section out completely, so it is off to one side, totally out of line with the box. To reassure his audience, he opens the portholes again. His assistant is still smiling cheerfully, tapping her feet, and she waves her left hand from its impossible new position.

The magician finally pushes the box back into place, removes the blades, and helps his unharmed assistant out from the cabinet.

How can this be?

SOLUTION ON PAGE 212

ALEXANDER

CRYSTAL SEER

Sees
Your Life
from the
Cradle

to the
Grave

THE GREAT HOUDINI has concealed 10 differences in the opposite picture. Can you find them?

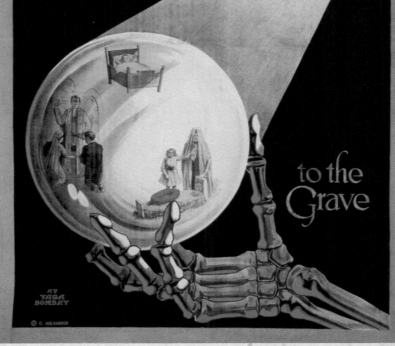

ALEXANDER

CRYSTAL SEER

Sees
Your Life
from the
Cradle

to the
Grave

SOLUTION ON PAGE 213

133

CENTRAL SPACING

A **BASIC GRASP** of how various materials react to different environmental stresses is vital for anyone hoping to become proficient in illusionism. Even with card tricks, you'll need to know exactly how the cards bend and flex, what their limits are, how flammable they are, and so on. For escapology, it's of critical importance to have a solid knowledge of metallurgy.

So take a moment to think about a coin with a hole in the centre. It's common knowledge that metal expands when it is heated. So if you heat that coin, what happens to the hole in the middle – does it shrink or grow?

SOLUTION ON PAGE 214

HOUDINI'S RADIO ILLUSION

For this trick, Houdini made use of a hugely oversized mock radio cabinet. It was about six feet wide, and a couple of feet deep and high, with massive dials and tuner bar. The thing was on a table with long legs that had black cloth skirting, which fell about halfway down to the floor. Once some porters had brought the thing in and placed it in the middle of the stage, he would lift up the cloth for a minute to show the audience that there was nothing underneath, and then unlatch the front and rear panels of the radio to demonstrate that there really was nothing inside it, apart from the few bits of wiring and tubing required to provide some basic radio functions.

Once he'd closed the cabinet back up, he activated the radio, and fiddled with the dials until he could tune in to some music. At that point, the top of the radio would open, and his assistant stand up out of it.

Where did she come from?

SOLUTION ON PAGE 214

THE SÉANCE

LATER ON IN his career, Houdini devoted a large amount of his free time to unmasking fraudulent mediums, people who preyed financially on the grieving. Many of the techniques used in stage magic were commonly employed by these "physical trance" mediums, including rope bindings, curtained cabinets and misdirection. A few tricks were even lifted wholesale in one direction or the other.

An example of this is the Séance Table. In this illusion, the magician gathers a group of people around a circular table. They lay their hands flat on it and concentrate, and suddenly the table starts floating, bobbing as it rises into the air. Before they can properly react, it is lifting wildly. The magician is seemingly lost in trance as the table whirls and spins around the room under the influence of his power, his hands clearly placed flat on its surface throughout.

How is it done?

SOLUTION ON PAGE 214

The
PEDESTAL

THE GREAT HOUDINI approaches a small pedestal on the stage. After some patter about his mystic abilities, he has a pair of assistants standing either side of the pedestal hold up a sheet. After a few suitably enigmatic movements, he gestures for them to drop it again. On the pedestal is a third woman.

Where does she come from?

SOLUTION ON PAGE 214

PUZZLE CHAIN

FIRST LINK

THE GREAT HOUDINI is caught in a final chain of puzzles. To save him, you will have to work your way through the chain, making careful note of your answers to each link. You'll need them all if you're going to successfully open the cunning puzzle lock that binds him. For the greatest challenge, do not check to see if your answers are correct until after you've completed the final lock.

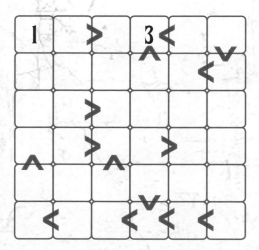

Each row and column of this grid contains the numbers 1–6 once exactly. The chevrons (">" signs) between cells indicate that the number on the wide side of the chevron is larger than the number on the pointed side. The number in the bottom right-hand corner is the value of the first link.

SOLUTION ON PAGE 215

SECOND LINK

PUZZLE CHAIN

	9	8			8	2		5	
									9
	4	6					7		
			10						
					3				
					1				
	4						11		
2	6		7	11	1		3	10	5

Each number in the grid above is connected to its identical partner by an unbroken line of cells. These lines never bunch to form a two-by-two (or larger) square. When the grid is filled correctly, every square is used. The value of the first link will give you the number of extra squares needed to correctly connect the two 3s.

The value of the second link is equal to the number of squares in the line connecting the two 6s, including the start and end square. What is it?

SOLUTION ON PAGE 215

PUZZLE CHAIN

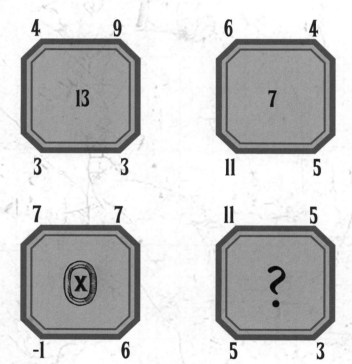

The values of these squares follow a certain specific logic, if you can uncover it. The value of the second link in the chain will tell you how much X is worth.

The number that should replace the question mark is the value of the third link of the chain. What is it?

SOLUTION ON PAGE 216

FOURTH LINK

PUZZLE CHAIN

This system of weights is in perfect balance. You may assume that beams and struts are rigid and weightless. The value of the third link in the chain will tell you how much X is worth. How much does the right-most weight weigh?

SOLUTION ON PAGE 216

PUZZLE CHAIN

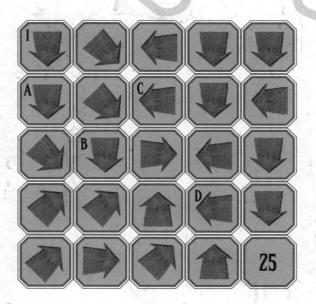

The aim of this numeric maze is to work your way from square 1 to square 25, stopping exactly once at each other square on the way. You can move any distance from the square you are on, but only in the precise direction indicated by the arrow.

Number the squares in the sequence you land on them, starting from square 1. The value of the first link in the chain will give you the correct sequence number of the square in the bottom left of the maze. There is only one correct route.

The letters A to D in the grid stand for the values of the first through to the fourth links respectively, so A = the value of the first link, B = the value of the second link, and so on. These values tell you the number in the sequence that the square in question occupies.

Can you complete the grid and free Houdini?

SOLUTION ON PAGE 216

142

BERTRAND'S BOX

WE HAVE TALKED elsewhere about the importance of probability. In a work in 1889, a French mathematician named Joseph Bertrand formulated a quintessential test of probability theory that remains popular today. Imagine that there are three identical boxes (or bags, if you prefer). Each box contains two coins. In one box, both coins are silver. In the second, both coins are gold. In the third, there is one coin of each.

You are blindfolded, and the boxes are mixed up. You select a box, and receive a coin from that box, chosen entirely at random. The coin you get is gold.

What is the chance that the other coin in that same bag is also gold?

SOLUTION ON PAGE 216

THE HAT

THE GREAT HOUDINI selects an innocent member of the audience to come and provide some assistance. Once the volunteer has been introduced, she is asked to select a card at random from a deck fanned downwards. Once she takes a card and memorizes it, she puts it back into the deck. The magician shuffles the deck thoroughly.

Once the cards are properly mixed up, he drops them one by one into a top hat until the whole deck is in there. Then he produces a length of rope, and announces that he's going to fish her very own card out of the hat with the aid of his powers. He drops the rope into the hat unsuccessfully a couple of times, and then the next time, incredibly, when he whips the rope out, the card she selected is actually tied to the end.

How does he do it?

SOLUTION ON PAGE 217

HOUDINI'S STRAITJACKET *Escape*

EVEN TODAY, HOUDINI is associated with escaping from straitjackets. He first began this feat during his handcuff escapes at police stations. Standard-issue police straitjackets are heavy things, made from thick canvas that's been reinforced with leather. The arms are more like sacks, without openings at the ends, and several times longer than a sleeve would normally be so that they can be wrapped around the body. The whole thing is secured with multiple straps.

Over the course of his straitjacket escapes, Houdini managed to get the time he needed to escape from one down from half an hour to less than three minutes. He also started performing this feat whilst hanging upside down, often over dangerous terrain with a burning rope providing a literal deadline. For these escapes, he used slightly modified straitjackets that, whilst still effective restraints, were somewhat easier to get out of, having fewer buckles and slightly more slack in the arms.

Although he didn't cheat at his straitjacket escapes, there were two physical actions Houdini could take when being placed into a straitjacket to make sure it was easier to get out of. Do you know what they are?

SOLUTION ON PAGE 217

START

END

SOLUTION ON PAGE 218

SIDEWAYS

AS SHOULD BE thoroughly obvious by now, mastery of illusionism requires a tendency for lateral thinking, and often the sneakier the better. Sometimes, it can be better to start at the back of a problem and work forwards rather than vice versa. Other times, you have to reframe the matter completely in order to get to the heart of it.

With that said, imagine the Great Houdini is standing on a stage somewhere in New York. He is holding a perfectly ordinary chair leg. It really is ordinary, too – just a solid cylinder of wood of the sort used to support chairs all over the world. Casually, he throws the leg away.

After travelling a short distance, the chair leg slows, stops in mid-air for an instant, then flies back to him, and he catches it easily. The chair leg does not bounce off anything at any point. It does not have any elastic attached to it, nor anything else for that matter. The wood it is made from is a perfectly regular chunk of mahogany. No one swaps it out midway, or anything like it. In fact, the leg is not interfered with at all by anyone at any point.

How does he do it?

SOLUTION ON PAGE 218

SEPARATION ANXIETY

THE GREAT HOUDINI draws the audience's attention to a stack of three boxes on the stage. As is often the case with boxes used in illusions, these have portholes placed variously, sealed with little flaps. He opens the fronts of the boxes, and demonstrates that together, they make a sort of cabinet. He helps his assistant into the space, and closes the fronts. Then he unlatches the portholes to show her face, hand and foot.

Once the portholes are sealed, he casually lifts the top box, #1, off the stack, and carries it to the other side of the stage. He sets it down, opens the porthole, and her head is there, smiling at him. He closes the porthole again, moves back to the other two, and opens the porthole of the box that had been in the middle, #2. Sure enough, there's her hand. Frowning, he latches the box and places it in a spot near the centre of the stage. He opens the #2 porthole again, and her hand waves at him. He closes it, and goes to the third box, #3, which has yet to move. He opens it, and her face grins at him. He closes it, darts across the stage, and opens the #1 porthole. Her toes wiggle at him. He slams it closed again, then whips it up and places it on the #2 box, and then tops it with the #3 box. Smiling, his assistant steps out.

How?

SOLUTION ON PAGE 219

The
LOTTERY

FOR THIS TRICK, the Great Houdini calls up an innocent volunteer from the audience. Once they're properly introduced, he has the volunteer sit at a table to operate a raffle drum, which is glass-barrelled so everyone can see inside it. It contains balls marked with the numbers 1 to 75, once each. The magician explains that his volunteer will operate the machine without any interference from him, and draw out five numbers.

Thanks to his amazing psychic powers, the magician already knows what the numbers are, and he has placed a slip of paper containing them into one of half a dozen balloons being held by his assistant. Once the numbers have been chosen, he'll prove it.

So the volunteer dons a blindfold and picks five balls from the raffle drum. The audience can see that the process is not being interfered with. Once it is complete, Houdini thanks the volunteer, and then walks over to his assistant to collect the balloons from her. Once they're in his grasp, he shakes them, one by one, until he finds the one that rattles, showing the paper is inside. He flourishes a pin and pops it, and the paper falls into his open hand. Picking it up slowly so there's no doubt in anyone's mind, he shows the volunteer and everyone else that he has indeed predicted the correct numbers.

How?

SOLUTION ON PAGE 219

Do Spirits Return?

HOUDINI

SAYS NO - AND PROVES IT
3 SHOWS IN ONE
MAGIC-ILLUSIONS-ESCAPES = FRAUD MEDIUMS EXPOSED

LYCEUM THEATRE
PATERSON
THURS., FRI., SAT. SEPT. 2·3·4
MATINEE SATURDAY

THE GREAT HOUDINI has concealed 10 differences in the opposite picture. Can you find them?

SOLUTION ON PAGE 220

The
EXQUISITE CORPSE

THE GREAT HOUDINI displays to the crowd an easel covered with a thick canvas sheet, and a large pad of art paper. He calls up three innocent members of the audience to provide him with help, and after introductions, he explains. The paper in the pad is divided into thirds horizontally, so that it is in fact a pad of three sets of strips. On the top set of strips, he has drawn a wide variety of heads. On the middle set, an equally wide number of torsos, and on the bottom third, a similar variety of legs. To prove his point, he opens the covers and flips a number of pages open to a collection of quite random images.

He then informs the volunteers that they are going to choose a composite image for him, but he already knows what they are going to pick. One by one, he has the volunteers step up and, as he flicks through the pages, tell him when to stop. He follows their instructions, and ends up with a peculiar chimera of a person. This is shown to the audience at large.

The magician whips the canvas off the easel and underneath is a painting of the exact chimera the volunteers have chosen.

How is this possible?

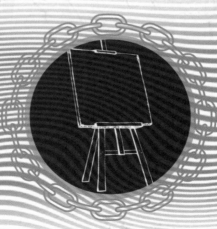

SOLUTION ON PAGE 221

TRICKY THINKING

THERE HAS BEEN much talk about the type of thinking required when dealing with stage magic and illusionism. So this puzzle provides a chance to put it into practice.

You are seated at a table that holds twenty coins. The coins are laid out flat, in a rough rectangle, a random mixture of heads and tails. Each of the coins has been marked on one side only with a fluorescent dye that is totally undetectable to you in the current circumstances. Coins had their heads or tails side marked randomly, so you can't draw any conclusions from the sides that are facing up – although for the record, you can see 12 heads and 8 tails.

All that you know is that at the moment, exactly ten of the marked sides are facing up, and the other ten are facing down. Their distribution through the group of coins is entirely random.

In other words, you have no way to tell which coins are marked-side up. How would you go about sorting the coins into two sets of ten, where both sets have the same number of marked sides facing upwards?

SOLUTION ON PAGE 221

The
MAGIC MAT

THE MAGICIAN PLACES a coin on a solid rubber mat, and declares that with his mystic powers, he is going to make the coin slip through the rubber on to the table beneath. He places his hand flat over the coin, and rubs vigorously, chanting some mystical-sounding nonsense. Then he lifts his hand back up, still perfectly flat, and shows that the coin is gone – and it's not in his hand, either. Then he asks an innocent volunteer to lift off the mat and, lo and behold, the coin is in place beneath it.

How does he do it?

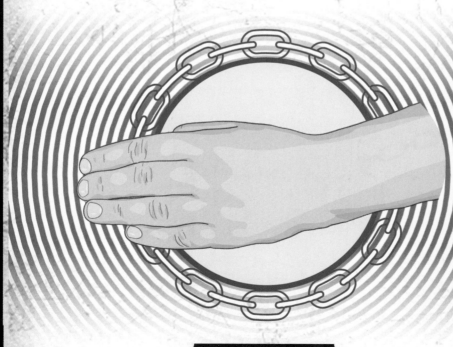

SOLUTION ON PAGE 222

ESCAPE
THE MAZE

START

END

SOLUTION ON PAGE 222

HOUDINI'S MILK CAN ESCAPE

HOUDINI ACTUALLY DESCRIBED this feat as "the best escape that I have ever invented", and posters for it gave grave warnings about the potential it offered for a horrible water death.

The milk can that he escaped from was made of metal, with a lid that attached to the can's collar in six different places. Audience members were invited to come and inspect the can, feel around inside it, kick at it, and finally, whilst he was changing into a swimming costume, fill it to the brim with water.

Once it was ready, he climbed inside it, submerging his head. If any extra water spilled out, this was topped off. Then the lid was placed on top. The six hasps were fitted over the collar's tongues and secured in place with heavy padlocks, including locks provided unseen by members of the public, if any were available. Then a screen was placed around the can.

Two minutes later, soaking wet and panting for agonized breaths, Houdini would stagger around the screen. When the screen was removed, the can was exactly as it had been left, including the padlocks all remaining firmly in place.

How did he do it?

SOLUTION ON PAGE 223

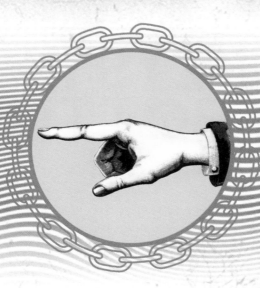

THE FINGER RIPPER

THE MAGICIAN TAKES a length of thin rope, and demonstrates that it truly is perfectly normal in every respect. An innocent member of the audience is invited up to examine it. Then the magician's assistant is called over, and the rope is looped around her little finger. The magician explains that he is going to magic the rope straight through her finger. It has the potential to go horribly wrong and tear her finger right off, but because of the training both of them have undergone, all will be well.

The volunteer is given one end of the rope to hold firm, and told not to waver in his grip even the slightest. If he fails, all sorts of disaster may ensue. The magician holds the other end, and on the count of three, yanks the rope brutally. Incredibly, it slips right through the assistant's finger without causing any damage.

How?

SOLUTION ON PAGE 223

KEYS IN A BOTTLE

THE GREAT HOUDINI gathers a crowd of spectators around himself, and picks one from amongst their number. After getting some basic introductions from the volunteer, he produces an empty but sealed wine bottle, and shows it to the group, even lets them touch it. It is perfectly regular. Then he asks the volunteer to hand him his bunch of house keys. The volunteer does so, somewhat nervously.

Houdini takes the keys, and shows them to everyone. He brings the wine bottle back up and presses the keys against it, clasping the bottle in both hands against his forehead as he concentrates on his mystical powers.

When he pulls the bottle back down, he shakes it. Metal is rattling inside. He drops the bottle onto the ground, breaking it. Everyone can see that the same keys are there in the broken bottle. The magician retrieves them carefully from the mess, and hands them back to the volunteer, who certifies that these truly are the same set of keys.

How is it done?

SOLUTION ON PAGE 224

THE
ESCAPE
Part Four

THE FRONT DOOR clicks open, and I step outside. It is a lovely day, warm and sunny. Looking around, I see that the garden I am in is quite extensive, and very well kept. The house that I have come from is significantly larger than the portion I have explored. I already suspected that would be the case from the size of the kitchen. Undoubtedly other doors – even other floors – were blocked away behind false partitions or larger pieces of furniture. That is of no moment. There is a letter addressed to me in the porch. I pick it up, open it and read.

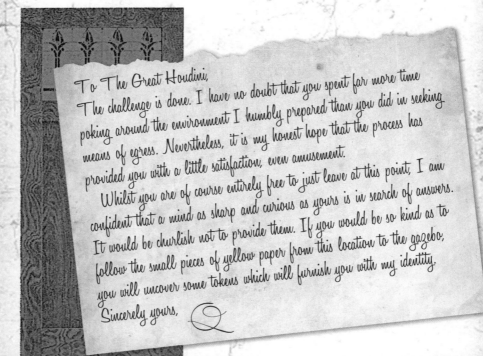

To The Great Houdini,

The challenge is done. I have no doubt that you spent far more time poking around the environment I humbly prepared than you did in seeking means of egress. Nevertheless, it is my honest hope that the process has provided you with a little satisfaction, even amusement.

Whilst you are of course entirely free to just leave at this point, I am confident that a mind as sharp and curious as yours is in search of answers. It would be churlish not to provide them. If you would be so kind as to follow the small pieces of yellow paper from this location to the gazebo, you will uncover some tokens which will furnish you with my identity.

Sincerely yours,

THE
ESCAPE
Part Four

I look around myself. There is indeed a small piece of yellow paper visible, next to a flagstone a couple of feet away. I walk to it, and spot another, a few yards ahead, next to an azalea. Following the breadcrumb trail is simple and Q is right, I would like some sort of answers. An attractive gazebo soon comes into view. It's a stretched octagon in shape, maybe six feet deep and fifteen feet across. It's lightly lacquered, giving the wood an elegant reddish-brown hue. The roof is made of wooden slats, stepping up to a row of windcatchers, which has its own little shingled roof. The doors have thin panels of glass running from top to bottom, two of them, separated by a vertical wooden strip. The handles are a little less than halfway up, level with a wooden divider that runs horizontally around the rest of the structure. That separates each of the other seven sides into two pieces. Panes of glass fill each space. I can't tell from this distance if some of them are openable windows, but I assume so.

Apart from the doors, the structure is surrounded by small bright flowerbeds. Hand-sized circular stones, placed three across, provide a charmingly higgledy-piggledy path leading to the doors. My eyes narrow as I see a jumble of objects inside the gazebo. They take up most of the space. I suppose these are to be my "tokens". One last challenge, is it? I am up to the task.

Most aware of the amount of material packed into the gazebo, I decide to start with the objects near the door, and work my way around the little space. So my first port of call is an expensive-looking dressing table. There are three mirrors that stand above the main flat surface of the table, a large central one with smaller ones to either side that can be swivelled to give different angles of reflection. Beneath the table surface are a number of small drawers, which turn out to hold a range of cosmetic devices, including hairbrushes, eyeliner brushes, cloths of various kinds, hairpins and slides, and other assorted accessories. The most interesting feature is the main body of the table, which lifts up to reveal all manner of little bottles and jars and small metal tools, each nested in its own velvet-lined compartment and filled with a dazzling variety of powders, creams, lotions and unguents. It's a lovely piece of work, and some lady not too far away is definitely looking forward to its safe return.

Beside the dressing table is a more rugged-looking work desk nestled in the gazebo's end-bay. It was varnished at some point in the past, but it has seen a lot of heavy use since then. Knife scars and small dents and dings abound, and in places, whole patches of the varnish have been abraded. The wood underneath is light, but sturdy – pine, most likely. It is supported by thick square legs quite unlike the delicate confections holding up the dressing table. I don't even need to examine the desk closely to be entirely confident that it is just five large, solid chunks of wood fastened together competently and securely. Pride of place is given to a vase of flowers in the middle. The vase itself is reasonably plain, but the flowers in it have been arranged attractively and competently. Daffodils play off tulips, primroses and hyacinths, with muscari scattered around for texture. The arrangement smells as lovely as it looks. Additionally, the table has a number of what appear to be gardening tools on it – wicked-looking secateurs, smaller trimming scissors, a pair of sharp knives and a hand trowel, accompanied by several plant pots, a bag of potting soil and a pair of leather gloves. But this is all secondary to the lovely flower display, honestly.

THE ESCAPE

Part Four

Emerging from my floral reverie, I force myself to continue exploring the contents of the gazebo. The next thing to claim my attention is a set of bookcases running along the back wall. They are well populated, but there are too many volumes to investigate each in any great detail. I'd be here for weeks. Instead, I settle for having a look at some of the books more or less at random. The first into my hand is a volume of poetry by Emma Lazarus, of whom it feels I have heard. Next is a history of canals and canal building, paying particular attention to the Gowanus Canal. This is followed by a novel set principally upon Coney Island, a book of statistics about the game of baseball, and a folio of paintings and sketches of locomotives from the past century. The final book I pick up is a biographical treatise about the England-born politician James Howell. All told, it's an impressive range of subjects and styles, and I'm certain I could find plenty of things in there to divert myself – if I were in the mood for further diversion, that is. As things stand, I have been quite sufficiently diverted from the norm today.

Stepping past the books and into the other of the gazebo's end-bays, I find myself face-to-face with something of a picture gallery. It takes me but a moment to recognize that all of the works on display are reproductions – surely, they are reproductions – of works by the genius Albrecht Dürer. The centrepiece of these is *Melencolia I*, a highly complex engraving featuring a winged and laurel-crowned woman in a flowing robe who appears to be having some difficulty with unspecified work. She holds a pair of compasses, with items at her feet that include an adze, nails and a wood saw. An incredibly complex magic square is engraved into the stone of

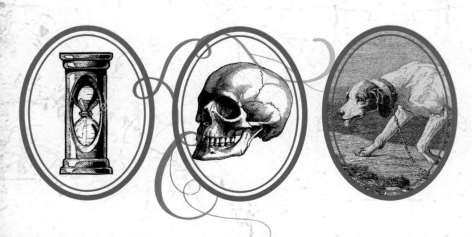

a wall above her head. There are a number of reminders of death in the piece, including a skull faintly visible in a peculiar trapezohedron, an hourglass whose sand is running down, an empty pair of scales, and a dog whose ribs are so pronounced that it is shortly close to starvation. A despondent cherub sits on a round object which might possibly be a deflated bellows. Other characteristic works of Dürer's hang around *Melencolia I*, including *Saint Jerome in his Study*; *Knight, Death and the Devil*; an early coloured self-portrait; an unsettling colour piece titled *Christ Among the Doctors*; and his drawing *Praying Hands*. It's an impressive collection, even as reproduction, but I cannot let it hold me indefinitely.

So I continue round the gazebo, and come to the last offering – a single suitcase, resting upon a simple table. It's quite plain, and there is little to be said for it other than I am certain it is perfectly serviceable. Inside, it is lined in a checked cloth. It holds a few items – just a small Victorian doll, a dog's collar and leash, and a man's bathing suit. It seems a somewhat despondent collection after the riches of the other areas.

However, it doesn't matter. Although I was doubtful initially, I now have no uncertainties regarding the matter of the mysterious Q's identity and intentions. I trust you can say the same?

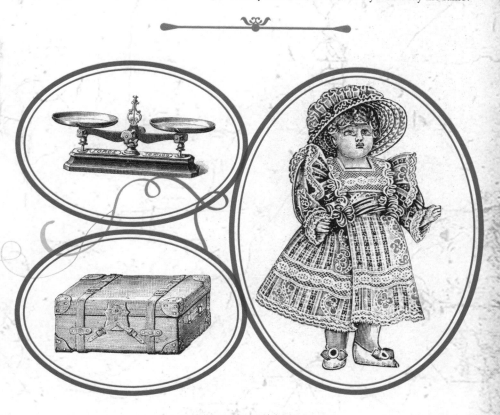

SOLUTION ON PAGE 224

SOLUTIONS

THE ESCAPE
Part One

Do you know yet how I made my escape? If not, then know that I needed precisely two of the items that were in the room, which I used to work upon the third. If you wish to return to the problem with this information in mind, please do not read further.

Very well. Escape really was quite simple. Hinges are every door's weak spot, particularly simple mortise butt hinges. Setting the point of the ice pick beneath the pin holding the two sections of hinge together, I used a brass bed knob to hammer on the base of the ice pick's handle. The pin came out easily. With the hinges removed, it was no challenge to pull that side of the door out of the frame, and then slide the whole door back. It remained locked, but the bolt is no bar when it is not in its hold. If minded to try a similar feat yourself, remember to unfasten the lower hinge first, and beware of injury, for doors can be surprisingly weighty.

THREADING THE NEEDLE

Tilt the barrel over until the water just touches the lip, and look into it. If it's less than half-full, some of the barrel's base will be visible. If it's more than half-full, some of the side wall will be submerged. Obviously, if the water exactly reaches the seam of the base, then it is precisely half-full.

THE WALK OF PENANCE

The secret is that despite your assumptions, broken glass is not all that dangerous under the right conditions. It's important to have enough depth to the layer of glass for the pieces to be able to shift and settle under your weight, and you have to let your feet feel around carefully for sharp points that might not move under pressure, but if you know what you're doing, it's perfectly safe. (If you know what you're doing, I repeat. Do not try this yourself without having expert guidance.)

HANDCUFFS

The simple answer is that Houdini studied handcuffs obsessively. He not only knew all the different models available, he had his own pairs of them, along with keys to them all. He only needed to glance at the cuffs to know which key he'd need to get out of them, and he made sure to check what he was going to be faced with before the show, so he could secrete the keys around himself and his stage as necessary.

On the few occasions where he was presented with one-of-a-kind cuffs, Houdini would perform a thorough inspection to ensure the cuffs would actually fasten and unlock, and so on. Whilst he did so, an assistant would go and search the magician's vast selection of keys for one that looked like the 'freak' handcuffs' key. Then he'd surreptitiously pass this fake to Houdini, who'd give it back to the owner of the cuffs whilst keeping the real key for himself. He'd then switch the keys back after his escape. Never forget that stage magic is deception.

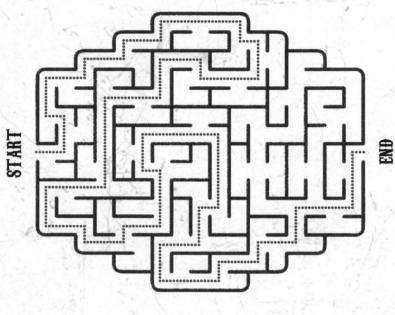

START

END

EXPERTISE

Houdini switches over the scrap of paper after the games are done, and the total of the remaining pieces is known. Depending on circumstances, either one of the chess players could jot down the correct number and pass it to Houdini during his congratulations, or the magician could surreptitiously write down the correct number himself. Either way, before he asks the adjudicator to pick up the scrap of paper, it has been replaced whilst everyone's attention was misdirected elsewhere.

NAILED

None of the covered cups have a nail in. Whilst fitting the lid to the cup, Houdini swiftly slides the nail back out and palms it. No matter which cups the volunteer selects, the magician knows he is perfectly safe. At the end of the trick, he just lets the nail fall back into his hand as he pulls the last cup apart.

BLOWN AWAY

The deck is a trick deck. Fanned on one end, it only actually contains eight different cards. Riffling swiftly, people are too busy trying to see a card to select to notice the repetitions. It's a fine line to get this correct, but practice makes perfect. Then it's easy to narrow down the correct pick from eight possibilities to one with the help of a couple of leading 'psychic perceptions' and studying the volunteer's reactions. What about afterwards? When fanned from the other end, the deck does not contain any of the eight cards. Of course hers is missing.

SPOT THIS

MIND THE TANK

Anything that sinks in water has to be denser than water. That means, by definition, that it takes up a smaller volume than its equivalent weight of water. When the stone is in the bucket, it displaces an amount of water that weighs as much as it does. When the stone is in the water however, it only displaces an amount of water equal to its own volume. So the water level drops when you move the stone from the bucket to the tank.

RIVER RUN

For this trick, Houdini used a pair of gimmicked cuffs he called 'jumpcuffs'. They were strong enough to pass inspection, but little more. He only had to flex his wrists and they would pop open.

HEARTBEAT

All that this trick does is stop the pulse in the right arm. The heart keeps going perfectly normally, as usual. It's done by placing a crumpled sheet of paper or a smallish ball in the armpit. It should be big enough to fit completely in the hollow. Once that is in place, just press your arm firmly against your body. The object in your armpit will press against the artery leading into your arm, cutting off circulation. You'll get pins and needles, but to an observer it will seem as if your very heart has stopped.

START

END

INVISIBLE TOUCH

The audience – and the un-blindfolded volunteers – think that the trick begins when Houdini steps back and begins concentrating. But this is not true. There is a period of time between the subject being blindfolded and Houdini stepping out of reach. During this time, while the magician is showing his empty sleeve or jacket lining to everyone, he swiftly reaches out with his spare hand and taps the subject four times. Lacking sight, and with all the music and commotion, she doesn't know that everyone else thinks this is still the trick being set up.

FLOATING

The trick lies in the position of the feet. The magician uses the foot furthest from the audience to stand on tiptoe, whilst keeping the heel of that foot precisely level with the foot nearest the audience. The nearer foot obscures the further one, and the magician appears to be floating in the air. It's a very simple trick which relies heavily on correctly positioning both your feet and your audience, but it still takes substantial training to get your muscles used to moving that much weight around slowly and smoothly, with sufficient flex in your foot for your heel to seem straight.

WIRE-WALKER

The stick serves two purposes. Being quite weighty, it has reasonable inertia. If the wire-walker is edging towards one direction, pushing that direction with the stick will provide a counter-force which pushes him back up straight. More importantly, however, the stick brings the acrobat's centre of gravity down, generally below the level of the rope itself. From that position, the wire-walker is much more stable, as all of his weight will be serving to pull him directly down against the rope, even if a breeze makes him wobble.

CELL

He used the key. Before agreeing to a challenge, Houdini always insisted on a tour of the facilities, and in testing the door locks personally. Unknown to his would-be captors, he also brought along a small wax block, hidden in his palm. When he was given the key to try in the lock, he pressed it into the wax to make an imprint. Later, he used the imprint to make an exact duplicate. When the key he was given happened to be a master key to a row of cells, he was able to perform extra stunts to bedevil the locals.

FORCING CHOICE

Let's call our objects X, Y and Z, and say that X is the one we want to end up with. The volunteer selects two. That gives three possibilities. If he chooses Y and Z, we discard those two to end up with X. Otherwise, he chooses X and something else, and we discard the object he did not choose – Z, say. From there, he selects between the two remaining, say X and Y. If he then picks X, that is the one he ends with. If he selects the other, Y for example, then we discard that one too, to leave him ending up with X. Easy.

EXIT STRATEGIES

The solution is to have a different end to the trick for each possible option, a strategy now known as 'multiple outs'. So for example while a note saying, "You will select plate two!" is under the table, the folded up wad of paper she placed on the plate might have said, "You will select plate three!" if she'd unfolded it, and beneath plate one, there might be a note saying, "You will select plate one!" Some magicians go to extensive lengths to prepare multiple outs for a dizzying array of options.

NO PIT

None. The two pendulums will swing in perfect synchrony. Everything falls at the same speed in a vacuum, because gravity is, in effect, pulling every molecule of an object independently and simultaneously. This can be a strange idea to wrap your head around.

PUZZLE CHAIN

FIRST LINK

The symbol in the bottom left is worth 2.

SECOND LINK

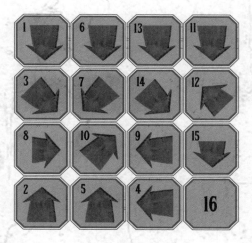

The sequence number of the top right square in the maze is 11.

THIRD LINK

The sum of the top two numbers minus the bottom left numbers gives you a value that when multiplied by the bottom right number equals the value in the centre. 19+15=34. 34-11=23. 23x2=46.

FOURTH LINK

The second grid is equivalent to 841,914 − 494533=347,381. The value in the bottom right square of the second grid is thus 1.

FINAL LINK

1	3	4	2	5 < 6
5 < 6	2 < 4	1	3
4 > 2	3 < 5	6	1
6	1	5	3	4	2
2	4	1	6	3	5
3	5	6	1	2	4

KEYMASTER

Houdini's hair was thick and shaggy, and offered a great hiding place for a small key, typically fixed in place near his skull with a little drop of adhesive. Since most prisoners are given short, simple haircuts, prison guards were less likely to think about how carefully they might need to comb through a thatch of unruly hair.

THE MENTALIST

The principle at work here is called one-ahead. The magician knows that the last choice is from one of three items, and by using forced choice, he can ensure that it will be one of the three in particular. So while the subject is choosing a colour, the magician writes down the object he intends to force – a watch, for example. Then the subject reveals his colour, and chooses a number. While he does so, the magician writes down the colour, which he now knows. Then the number is revealed. Finally, while the tray of items is being brought over to be forced, the magician writes down the number, and forces the watch, which he wrote down at the start. By upending the cup messily, he ensures that the predictions are not in a suspicious order.

FAMILIARITY

Your uncle.

EXIT

IN EXTREMIS

Knowing how rigorous the search would be, Houdini had Bess hide a copy of
the key under her tongue. She then slipped it to him in his farewell kiss.

HOUDINI'S CHINESE WATER TORTURE CELL

Since Houdini was lowered into the cell fairly rapidly, excess water splashed out as he entered. This provided a pocket of air to breathe. But the stocks were the key to the whole thing. When their hasps were latched to the tank, the pressure of this pulled the stocks apart a little. This was enough to let Houdini wriggle his feet through the holes. Then he turned himself the right side up, and took a breath from the top of the tank. The boards that the stocks were mounted on had well-hidden hinges, so that it was a simple matter to then push them up, like a saloon door, and exit. Then he just had to stand around patiently for a minute and forty-five seconds, to let the audience start really panicking.

A PAIN IN THE NECK

The trick makes use of a false loop. The ends of the chain are not crossed or tied. At the back of his neck, the magician makes a pair of short loops, one in each side of the chain, and then puts the loops within each other so that the whole thing stays in place. With the extra benefit of his hair to disguise matters, it looks as if he has genuinely looped the chain round his neck, but it's not true. When the assistants pull, the loops slip apart and the chain straightens.

NEVER FORGET

This time, the audience members are stooges, and in on the act. As soon as the curtain drops, they break their chain, and help the handler hurry the elephant behind a large mirror, placed just behind and to the side of the circle. From the audience seats, the mirror is invisible and that portion of the stage appears empty. The music obscures the sound of the elephant's steps. Then they dart back into place as the curtain falls to give the impression of an unbroken circle. The process is reversed for the reappearance.

DEATH ESCAPE

The weight is much lighter than the staggering assistants pretend – sheet steel, not a solid lump – and it was never attached to the neck chain to begin with. Instead, it is fastened to a catch on the straightjacket. Escaping from a straightjacket upside down is an impressive feat, but one that Houdini had practised so thoroughly that he could do it in seconds. Even so, for this trick, the jacket was generally unusually easy to slip out of.

THE BELL

Pack the bell with ice. This will immobilize the clapper, silencing the bell, at least until it melts. At that point, the bell will appear to be untampered with. Dry ice is even better, as it sublimates rather than melts, and so will not leave any water behind.

ESCAPE
THE MAZE

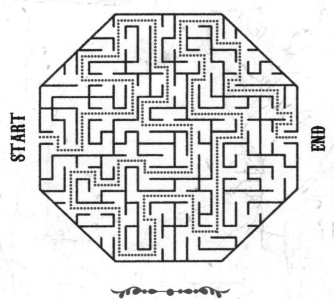

START

END

THE VANISHING ELEPHANT

The elephant didn't go anywhere. Houdini lied about the size of his cabinet, and lost in the middle of the largest stage in the world, with assistants selected for height, the audience couldn't really tell. While the cabinet was being rotated, the trainer ushered the elephant to one side, and a black cloth was put across where it now stood. With just ambient light entering the cabinet, and a clear view through, past the elephant, to the holes in the back doors, it looked as if the cabinet was empty.

THERE IS NO SPOON

The last audience member is a stooge who quickly pulls the spoon away and hides it whilst Houdini is flourishing the cloth.

TRAPEZE

The music. Any given trapeze routine is highly complex, but each piece is keyed to a specific moment in the score. So it is easy to know exactly when a particular set-piece is to begin. It is triggered by a particular note.

THE
ESCAPE
Part Two

If you are at something of a loss, then I shall reveal here that I used two items from two of the stations, and three from two more. I did cause a little damage in my escape, but nothing of any great moment. If you are now minded to return to the problem, please do so forthwith, for my next paragraph will reveal my technique.

As I mentioned before, the hinges are a door's weak spot. In this instance, the nearest equivalent to hinges are the two padlocks holding the grill in place. Padlocks are highly useful devices, but because of the limits of their size, they are not particularly sturdy. A good crowbar can easily defeat even a well-made one. I did not have a crowbar, but I did have the means to fashion a crude facsimile.

I took the pipe from the woodworking section over to the anvil, and hammered one end as flat as I could. It may have been that this would have proved sufficient, but I decided to attempt to do better. I gathered up a steel file and a flint hand-axe, along with a small heap of straw and spills of wood from the lid of one of the cases, which I did break. Using the flint and steel, it was easy to set fire to the straw and kindling, which I put on the anvil for safety purposes.

From that fire, I lit a spill of wood, and used it to light both the Bunsen burners. They were not particularly hot, but they were able to get the pipe at least glowing red. That – and the leather gloves – aided me in hammering my makeshift crowbar flatter, and in turning the end up creditably around the thin end of the anvil. Once it had cooled, it was easy to pass it through the padlock, brace the curled end against the wall, and place enough weight on the other end to force the padlock to give way. With both of them so opened, I could simply pull the bars out of the way.

I do not claim that this is the only possible solution that could have been found, but it is the one I settled on, and I do at least think it caused comparatively little damage.

THE UNDERWATER BOX

As previously discussed, the handcuffs were barely even an inconvenience. Houdini was typically out of those before his assistants had finished nailing the lid in place, even when they were provided by a third party. The secret of the box was that on one of the sides, the two lowest planks were not actually nailed in place. They had false nail-heads, but they were secured by a small latch inside the crate. Once under the water, Houdini unlatched the clasp and pushed the planks open, exiting comfortably, and used the ropes to hold himself down until enough time had passed. The ropes and chains were positioned to provide no inconvenience. On one occasion, the crate fell with the hinged hatch downward, and it took him a desperate minute of pushing to roll the crate over so he could escape. It was the last time he failed to exit the crate before it hit the bottom.

9

THE MIND READER

The paper has a small adhesive spot. Whilst he is pacing around, he brushes past the back of one of the chairs, and surreptitiously fixes the paper there. The chair's back obscures this from both audience and volunteer. Then he turns around and sweeps back past, glancing at the number, and collecting the paper back into his hand.

BULLET CATCHER

It's clearly impossible to stop a bullet with your bite, even if you somehow managed to get the timing microsecond perfect. You'd still be shot through the back of the throat, but your teeth would smash as well. The gun is loaded with a blank, and the glass is prepared with a specially weakened base, so that the discharge of gas from the muzzle is enough to make it shatter. Even so, the blank is aimed to the side of Houdini's actual face. The bullet he demonstrates at the end is in his mouth all along, hidden between gum and cheek.

BALANCE

The maximum overhang possible with a stack of books (or similar objects) under ideal conditions slowly diverges. The harmonic series, 1/1+1/2+1/3+1/4+1/5+... governs this particular calculation, and for a stack that is n books tall, the maximum overhang is one half of the sum of the first n terms of the harmonic series. With a stack of just four books, that gives you (1+0.5+0.333+0.25)/2, or a maximum overhang of 1+1/24ths – so the top book will be clear of the table.

WISDOM OF CROWDS

There's a stooge in the audience. Once Houdini is back on stage, the stooge just signals the two digits of the answer in some simple manner, perhaps with blinks of the left and right eye.

FLAT OUT

The carpet is fixed only on the side nearest the audience, and conceals a trench filled with soft foam. Houdini lies on this trench, which is only a little wider than his legs and hips, and extends from below his feet up to his shoulders. When the roller reaches him, it just pushes him down into the foam, with its weight at each side being borne by the regular stage flooring, because the roller is wide enough to span the trench. All he has to do is pretend to be in pain and, once the curtain falls, pull himself out.

HOUDINI'S METAL-RIMMED BOX

The trick to the box lies in its design. Although most of the planks making up the box are fixed to the metal rims, the bottommost ones are fixed only to the base, with its rim. The side rims appear to be firmly in place, but the box is held together by catches inside the box, cunningly hidden from view. Once inside, Houdini just releases the catches, and the box separates into two sections – the base, its rim, and the bottom row of planks forming one, and the rest of the top and sides (with the entire length of the side rims) forming the other. Then he just steps out, fits the box back together, and makes some noise for a few minutes.

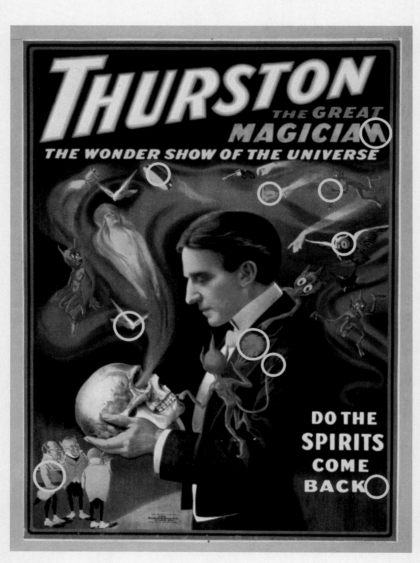

WALKING ON WATER

He's walking on clear glass, just under the surface of the water. Sometimes this might be a long spur of glass, like a pontoon, fixed to the tank. Other times, it might be glass posts coming up from the base of the tank. Either way, they are completely invisible inside the water.

LEVITATION

He's not holding on to the bus. The left arm is fake, and disguises a steel bar welded on to the side of the bus. The other side connects to a harness, which is what is actually holding him up.

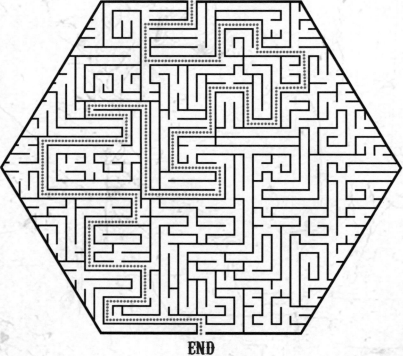

END

PATTERN RECOGNITION

Imagine a circle, with two guards setting off simultaneously from the top, one in each direction. It is obvious that they will meet part-way round. Similarly, there has to be a point in any circuit where the guard will always be at that same moment in his routine.

JEWELLERY

The glass moves. There is a hole hidden under the jeweller's cloth he rests his hand on, and a gap in the glass under the other. The cloths look normal, but are mounted on a thin, rigid base and pinned to the cabinet's wooden frame. A foot-operated switch shifts the glass across very swiftly, and from the audience's viewpoint, any motion is hidden by the frame. So the hole pops into place, he darts his hand through, and then he snaps the hole back under the fake cloth.

HOUDINI'S IRON BOX CHALLENGE

The bolts that Houdini used to attach the lid with were fake, with heads that in fact unfastened from the body of the screw. So it was just a moment's work to push the bolt bodies out and lift the top off. Once it was back in place, the bolts were pushed back inside, and fastened back together by reaching through the visibility holes.

PUZZLE CHAIN

FIRST LINK

The correct value of the right-hand weight, and of the first link, is 8.

SECOND LINK

9+4+5-8x3+10/2+4 = 24.

Four "+" signs means the second link is worth 4.

THIRD LINK

5	6	2	4	3	1
1	3	6	5	2 < 4
4	2	5	3 > 1	6
3	5	4	1	6	2
6 > 4	1	2	5	3
2 > 1 < 3 < 6	4	5

The third link is worth 1.

FOURTH LINK

1	6	6	6	6	6	6	6	6	6
1	6	1	1	1	1	1	1	1	1
1	6	1	7	7	7	7	7	7	1
1	6	1	5	8	9	9	9	7	1
1	6	1	5	8	2	3	9	7	1
1	6	1	5	8	2	3	9	7	1
1	6	1	5	8	2	3	9	7	1
1	1	1	5	8	2	3	9	7	1
5	5	5	5	8	3	3	9	7	1
8	8	8	8	8	4	4	4	7	1

Including both ends, the nine-line is 8 squares long, so that is the value of the fourth link.

FIFTH LINK

In each circle, each segment in the top half of the circle adds to the segment directly below it in the bottom half of the circle to sum to 13. 4+9=13, so the fifth link is worth 4.

SIXTH LINK

The values on the bottom scale are equivalent to 2+4=3+3, so the sixth link is worth 3.

SEVENTH LINK

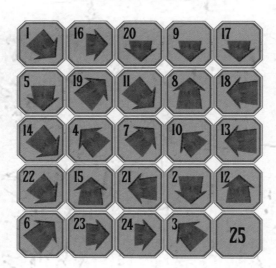

The bottom-left square is the sixth in the sequence, so the value of the seventh link is 6.

EIGHTH LINK

11	11	3	3	7	35
7	8	7	11	3	36
5	5	7	3	7	
8	3	5	8	8	32
8	5	11	5	11	
39		33	30		

The symbol in the top right – and thus the eighth link – is worth 7.

NINTH LINK

The numbers associated with each triangle form a sequence, starting with the topmost number and spiralling anticlockwise to end in the centre. The third triangle is part of the series of triangular numbers – the series that represents the continued summing of the natural numbers, so 0+1=1, 1+2=3, 3+3=6, 6+4=10, 10+5=15, and so on – but in this instance, running in reverse. The next term and the ninth link are equal to 3.

FINAL LINK

4	8	7	3	6	5	2	9	1
1	3	5	2	9	8	4	6	7
6	2	9	4	1	7	5	3	8
5	1	2	8	4	3	9	7	6
9	7	4	6	2	1	3	8	5
8	6	3	7	5	9	1	4	2
3	5	1	9	7	6	8	2	4
2	9	6	5	8	4	7	1	3
7	4	8	1	3	2	6	5	9

COMBINATOR

There are six dials, so six places where your definite "5" could be. That leaves five dials, which can make any number between 0 and 99,999–100,000 possibilities. So the odds of your getting the setting correct on a first try is 1 in 600,000.

HOUDINI'S
PLATE-GLASS BOX

The bolts holding the metal edges together were fake all along the back of the box. Although they appeared normal, the heads actually unscrewed from the shaft of the bolt. Well-hidden bits of thread or wire stopped the shafts from falling to the ground when the head (inside the box) was removed. So Houdini unscrewed the back, slipped out, unpicked the padlocks, opened the box and reassembled the back and its bolts, then closed the padlocks again. This took a bit longer than some escapes, but that only meant less time standing around waiting.

SPIDER-MAN

Wire. This trick is performed in the evening or at night, with the spotlight illuminating the magician from the front. The supporting wire is connected to a base much further back on the roof, out of sight, and it is surprisingly thin. The harness that attaches him to it is under his shirt and trousers, and the wire exits through the split for the jacket tails. It takes a lot of strength to pull off remaining horizontal and looking comfortable whilst dangling from a wire, even with a wall to walk down, so this trick is only for the very fit.

DISPLACEMENT

Their weights are identical. If an object floats, it displaces an amount of water whose weight is identical to its own weight.

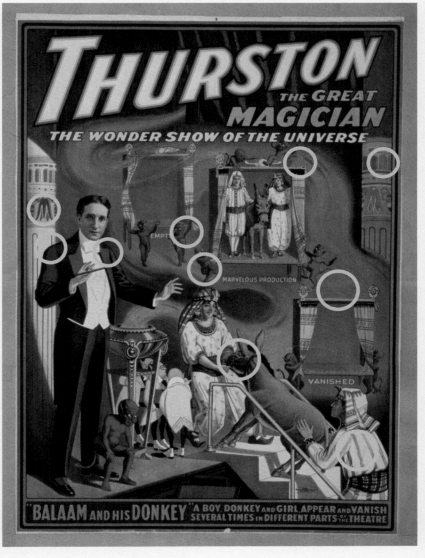

HOUDINI'S SPANISH MAIDEN ESCAPE

The hinges of the Maiden looked normal, but they were in fact ratcheted. By carefully taking hold of one of the spikes attached to the lid and lifting it slightly, the pins holding the hinges together would shift – and stick – slightly upwards. After enough lifts, the hinges would separate completely. Then Houdini just had to open the box, extract himself, and once the box was closed again, slip the pins back into the hinges for an undetectable escape.

THE SWITCH

Houdini is never in the air. As soon as his assistant throws the sheet to cover him, he swaps places with another assistant, made up to look as identical as possible to the first. Sometimes sisters were used. He hides in a space beneath the platform, using mirrors if necessary to disguise the fact that there is anything there. When his first assistant raises the sheet to cover herself, he crawls through her legs to stand in her place, and she hides where he was hiding. Then it's just a matter of dropping both sheets. With practice, the switch can be nearly instantaneous.

ESCAPE

THE MAZE

START

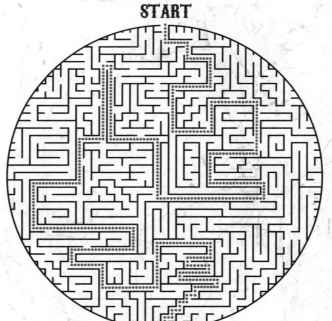

END

AN ILLUSION OF MAGICIANS

Robert. From the information given, Hermann must be the mentalist, Blackstone the rope specialist, Devant the coin trickster, Anderson the specialist in feats of daring, Maskelyne the card sharp, and Robert the escapologist.

DOING THE TWIST

His arm is already twisted through more than 180 degrees before he starts. So although he actually is turning it through 360 degrees, it is going from being flexed all the way to one side to being flexed part of the way on the other. Most people can't twist their arm 180 degrees or more without some flexibility training, so don't try to force the issue yourself, but with sufficient practice, the matter is easy.

HOUDINI'S EAST INDIAN NEEDLE TRICK

As should hopefully be obvious, Houdini never swallowed anything like needles. When he took the swig of water, he spat the loose needles and thread into the glass, where they were effectively disguised by the remaining water because of their thinness. The threaded needles were in a separate packet which he kept hidden in his mouth from the start. When he hooked his mouth open for the spectator to check, he tucked the packet under a finger. Definitely don't try this yourself – accidentally swallowing a needle would be very harmful.

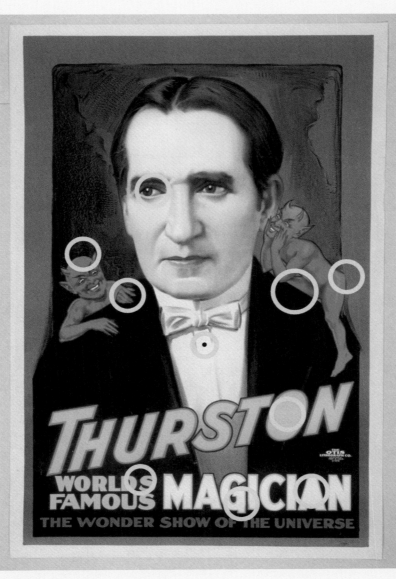

THURSTON

WORLD'S FAMOUS MAGICIAN

THE WONDER SHOW OF THE UNIVERSE

THE CIGARETTE

It's a trick coin with a flap over a central hole that recedes when pressure is put on it. The audience member who examines it is a stooge.

MALLEABLE

During the initial explanations, the magician replaces the borrowed coin with a trick one, specially prepared with a loose section that is held in place with a springy flap. While pretending to bite the coin, he just bends the loose piece back and hides it under his thumb. To replace the supposedly missing piece, he just lets go of it, and it springs back into place. Then he palms the trick coin again during his bow, and hands the original back to the volunteer.

I need only one item from my survey of the house. If that is not already clear to you, this is your chance to return and seek further illumination.

Very well. I am a master locksmith, after all. A hairpin is all that I need to pick an older lock, particularly a large one. I can even bend it back into approximately the correct shape afterwards. The front door poses no unusual challenges in that regard.

BEATING THE ODDS

If a coin is weighted, it is weighted towards returning either heads or tails. So whichever way it is stacked – or even if it is un-stacked – the chance of throwing a head followed by a tail will always be identical to the chance of throwing a tail followed by a head. So if you want to get a 50-50 result from a weighted coin, pick either HT or TH and throw the coin twice. If you get HH or TT, throw it twice again. The more blatantly the coin is weighted, the more throws it could take to get a pair which is one of each.

HOUDINI'S WALL PASSAGE

The carpet. There was indeed a trapdoor in the stage, a long, narrow one which ran across the stage, under the wall. As soon as the screen went up, the trapdoor opened, and the carpet sank into it, forming a trench. Houdini scooted quickly under the wall, hidden by the surface of the stage, and popped back up in time for the second screen to be removed.

THE FLY

Obviously, the fly isn't dead. It is deeply stunned by having been brought close to freezing. To all casual observation it appears completely dead. When the magician places it on his hand, the warmth of his flesh heats it back up again, and it recovers. The trick has to be done fairly swiftly after the fly is put in place, to avoid it waking up on its own.

THREE CUPS

Put one coin in the first cup, and then two coins and the first cup into the second cup. The first cup thus holds one coin, and the second cup holds three. This leaves seven coins to go into the third cup. There are other combinations of course, but they all follow the same basic principle that one cup and its odd number of coin/s have to go inside another cup with an even number of coins, leaving an odd number for the remaining cup.

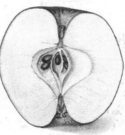

FRUITY

The deck isn't regular. Many of the cards are missing, including all the ones that people commonly think of, like the jack of diamonds, queen of hearts, or ace of spades. The deck is made to look convincing, with multiple copies of the cards that are in there. There is a little luck involved, but not much, as few people pick cards outside the typical top twenty. If she does pick one of the cards that is present, the magician just takes the indicated card and moves on to a different way out. Meanwhile, all possible missing cards are already pre-rolled tightly, ordered precisely, and placed somewhere convenient – often under the table that holds the fruit bowl, disguised by mirror placement, although it's also possible to work them into the stage clothing. It's not difficult to palm the correct card whilst selecting a piece of fruit. Then the card is just sleighted into the fruit as it is cut, so it can be pulled out and unrolled.

LACED

The shoes are properly laced to begin with, but the bow is tucked away behind the trouser leg. An identical shoelace is positioned over the bow, obviously loose, the ends hanging down. This lace is fixed to a piece of string, which runs up the inside of the trouser leg to a small handle in the trouser or jacket pocket. As the magician shakes his leg, he tugs on the string, pulling the loose shoelace up his trouser leg. The effect is that he seems to have tied his shoelace by shaking his foot.

GOING WRONG

There are several phases to this trick. The first is that the magician has to force the volunteer to select the correct card. There are several ways to do this, but the most common is the "classic force", done by slowing the card riffle down a little to highlight one particular card for the subject. Once the card is back in the back, a copy of that card is palmed, and when the top card of the deck is shown to be the wrong one, the magician actually has two cards in his hand. So when he puts them back on the deck and then takes the top off again, it's the card he had palmed – the duplicate of the volunteer's card. This is ripped quickly and pressed into the volunteer's hand before it can be seen. The next card on the deck is, of course, the same "wrong" card that was there before. Then when he takes the torn card back from the volunteer, he has a third, folded copy of the card palmed, and after showing the ripped one to everyone, passes back the folded copy. Then all he has to do is get the volunteer to unfold the third copy of the card she thought she had freely picked.

ON THE RADIO

The radio is firmly fixed to the silver tray. The assistant takes it away when she removes the tray, angling it as she leaves to keep the radio hidden. The cloth retains its convincing shape through the use of small rods sewn into the underside of the fabric. When the cloth is whipped, these slip out of alignment, giving no sign to the audience that they were ever there.

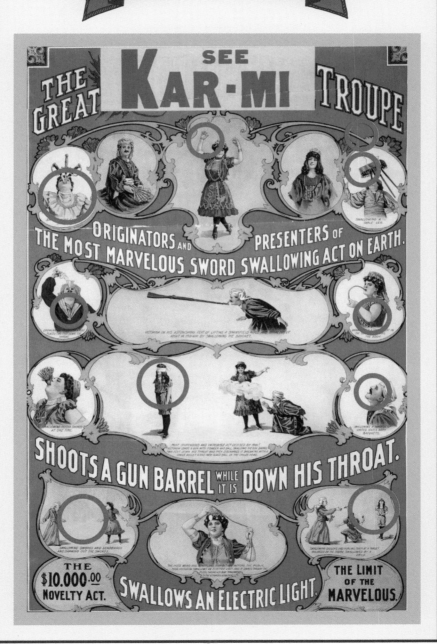

CHAINS OF LOGIC

Yes, because tricks I don't understand make me mutter.

HOUDINI'S METAMORPHOSIS

Houdini was very well practised at getting out of restraints, and was out of the rope binds before the bag was up to his shoulders. The rope fastening the bag ran alternately inside and outside the bag because it was threaded through ringlets, so he pulled a length of it down into the bag and held it there while it was sealed. This gave him the slack necessary to be out of the bag almost as soon as the top of the box was closed. The box, in turn, had a false back, so even as it was being locked, he was slipping out of the back. As soon as the cabinet was in place and the curtain closed, he took his wife's place, and started clapping. By the time he'd finished, she'd already re-entered the box and re-latched the back panel. Then as he started unlocking the box, she wriggled into the bag, pulled the top rope tight, and then slipped her hands into the ropes where he'd left them.

THE SPINNING ASSISTANT

The pedestal is hollow, and has a pair of hatches where the box, also hatched, connects. As soon as the magician closes the bottom view-hole, his assistant squeezes out of the box and into the space of the pedestal. Once he's finished rotating the box, she opens the other hatch and gets back up into the pedestal.

FLOATING FOOD

The can is gimmicked with a small hole in the back. The magician pops his thumb in there when he picks it up, and pretends first to be holding it with his fingertips, and then to be levitating it.

THE DIVIDED GIRL

First, the blades are extremely flexible. As the magician pushes them into the cabinet, his assistant pushes them downwards, so that once they are in place, they both point straight down. Secondly, when the magician pushes the mid-section of the box, all he is actually moving is the front panel. There's a slanted mirror behind it, reflecting what appears to be the back of the stage. The audience think they're looking straight through, but it's just not true. The presence of the mirror makes the box a little cramped, and when the portholes are opened, the assistant has to cross her left hand over her body to stick it out of the hole whilst simultaneously smiling in apparent comfort, but it's perfectly achievable with a bit of practice and natural flexibility. Then it's just a matter of waiting for the blades to be removed and the door opened.

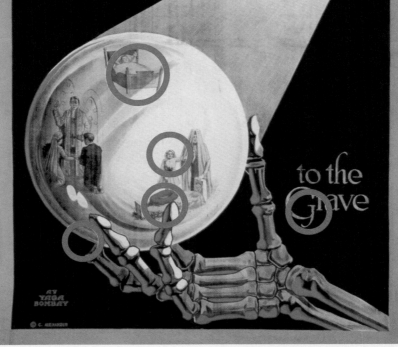

CENTRAL SPACING

The hole gets larger, because the metal keeps the same proportions. So heating a nut without heating the screw its threaded on will loosen it.

HOUDINI'S RADIO ILLUSION

The table that the cabinet rested on had a "bellows-top", effectively two tops that could open a short distance – in this case, just a little less than the depth of the black cloth skirting. When the cabinet was brought in, the assistant was already inside. Once Houdini showed off the space beneath the table and re-covered it, she activated the bellows top, and used a hatch to get into the space between the two tops. So Houdini was then able to show off the empty interior. As soon as he re-closed the cabinet and started tuning the radio, she came back through the hatch, pulled the bellows partition closed, and then opened the lid and came on out.

THE SEANCE

The magician is wearing a brace on his forearm with a retractable metal bar built into it. When he puts his hands on the table, he pushes the bar into a socket fastened to the underside of the table. Although it is stained to look like mahogany or something similar, the table is actually made of balsa wood, and is extremely light. With his hands on the top to steady it, it's simple to lift it with his arm and swoop it around the room.

THE PEDESTAL

The pedestal is hollow, with a hinged lid, and covering a trapdoor to a space beneath the stage. When the sheets go up, the third assistant pulls down the lid, climbs up out, latches it again, and stands on the pedestal in a suitable pose.

PUZZLE CHAIN

FIRST LINK

1	4 > 2	3 < 6	5
5	1	4	6	2 < 3
6	5 > 3	1	4	2
3	6 > 5	2 > 1	4
4	2	6	5	3	1
2 < 3	1 < 4 < 5 < 6

The first link is worth 6.

SECOND LINK

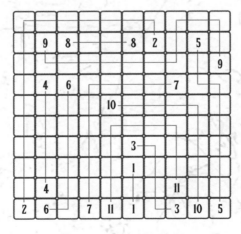

The second link is worth 8.

THIRD LINK

The top two numbers are multiplied (11*5=55), and the result summed with the bottom left number (55+5=60). This total is then divided by the bottom right number. (60/3=20). So the third link is worth 20.

FOURTH LINK

On the left side, the pressure is (12+9)*8=168 units. On the right, $2*(X=20)=40$, leaving the final weight to account for 168-40=128 units. 128/8=16, the value of both the right-most weight and the fourth link.

FINAL LINK

BERTRAND'S BOX

The chance of getting a second gold coin is 2/3. This is because there are three gold coins you could have originally received. Call them B1, B2, and C. Your chance of getting any one of the three is identical, so once you know the coin is gold, the three probabilities are the same. In two of those cases, B1 and B2, the other coin is gold. Only if you got C originally is the other coin silver.

THE HAT

Magnets. Specifically, the hat already contains a second piece of rope with the card tied to it. There are magnets in the ends of both pieces, so while he's fishing, all he needs to do is bring the ends together. Because he whips the rope out, he can grab the place where the ends meet before anyone sees its magnetic join. As to the card being the right one, the solution to that is the simplest force there is – the entire deck is the same card.

HOUDINI'S STRAITJACKET ESCAPE

Houdini's practice at holding his breath over the years had given him massive lung capacity, so one physical aid he used was to inflate his chest as much as possible while the jacket was being fitted. This gave him a fair amount of slack to work with. Then, wherever possible, he folded his arms over his chest rather than crossed them. This removed the complication of the crossed sleeves forming another knot. If he was forced to cross his arms though, the second physical action he was able to do was to dislocate either or both of his shoulders to wiggle loose of the sleeve-knot. Either way, it was then a matter of practice in bringing the arms out of the sleeves, unfastening their buckles with his mouth, and then using his freed hands to unbuckle the chest, torso and neck clasps. Reaching his level of skill in defeating straitjackets took many years of dedicated physical training.

START

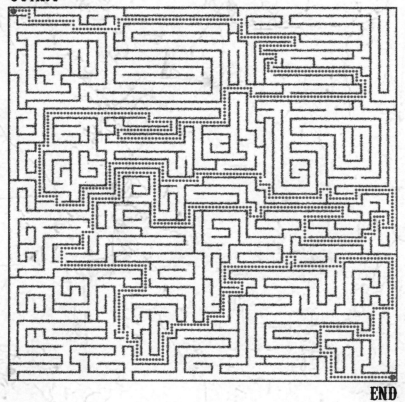

END

SIDEWAYS

He throws it straight up. We did warn you that sneakiness – sideways thinking
– was needed.

SEPARATION ANXIETY

All it takes are some carefully placed trapdoors, boxes with tops and bottoms that fold out of the way, a couple of feet of space under the stage roofed with climb-bars so she can pull herself around down there very quickly, and many, many hours of exhaustingly athletic practice. Getting just the foot to appear in a one-high stack is the toughest feat, and requires (a) very flexible ankles and (b) turning feet-on to the audience.

THE LOTTERY

The balloons are all empty. As the volunteer draws the balls, the assistant writes them down surreptitiously. She passes the paper to the magician when he collects the balloons from her, and he palms it. When he's ready to pick a balloon to pop, he lets it rattle against the paper in his hand to counterfeit sounding like there's something inside, and as it pops, he lets it drop into his hand.

SPOT THIS

Do Spirits Return?
HOUDINI
SAYS NO AND PROVES IT
3 SHOWS IN ONE
MAGIC-ILLUSIONS-ESCAPES = FRAUD MEDIUMS EXPOSED
LYCEUM THEATRE
PATERSON
THURS. FRI. SAT. SEPT. 2 3 4
MATINEE SATURDAY

THE EXQUISITE CORPSE

The pad is in two sections. The first section includes all of the genuinely varied illustrations that the magician shows off at the start. The second section has only identical illustrations on each set of strips, and this is the section he flicks through when allowing the volunteers to choose their contributions. Since he knows what they will pick, preparing the image in advance is trivial. The two sections may just switch over halfway through, or be arranged upside down and back to front, or even be in two separate pads where one is switched out for the other. It depends on the magician's preferences.

TRICKY THINKING

Forget the heads and tails – the coins might as well be featureless. Divide the group into two equal groups of 10, A and B, however you like. Since you know that exactly 10 of the 20 are marked-side up, then if group A has X marked sides up, group B must have 10 X- marked sides up, and thus 10-(10-X) = X-marked sides down. So if A has 4 marked up, B has (10-4=) 6 marked up, and (10-6=) 4 marked down. Turn all the coins in B upside down, and the two groups are guaranteed to have the same number of marked sides facing upwards.

THE MAGIC MAT

The coin beneath the mat is there right from the start, of course. The other coin was pushed off the table by the rubbing motion, into the magician's other hand. It's easy to do. During the part of the circular rubbing stroke that is moving towards the magician, he presses his hand on to the coin to move it towards him. During the other part, moving back up towards where the coin started, he lifts his hand away from it. After a few rubbing motions, the coin is pushed straight back off the table.

START

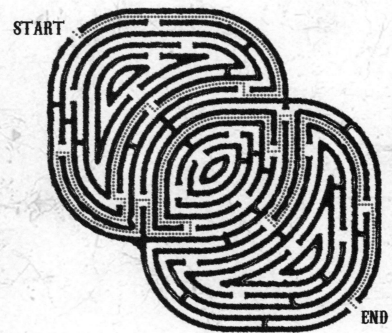

END

HOUDINI'S
MILK CAN ESCAPE

The collar was not actually attached to the neck of the can. Although it was impossible to budge the collar from the outside, from inside the can it could be pushed up with trivial ease, taking the lid – and the locks – with it. Houdini was out of the milk can almost before the screen had stopped vibrating from being set down.

THE FINGER RIPPER

The rope is looped round the assistant's finger from below, not above. So long as she keeps her finger totally relaxed, the pressure from below will jerk her finger down so the rope slips off. Her finger snaps back into place on the rebound. It all happens so fast that it's invisible to the naked eye, giving the impression that the rope passed through her. Note that the rope has to be the right thickness and weave to provide enough pressure to overcome skin friction painlessly, and that getting the loop wrong will cause the assistant a lot of pain, so don't try this unless you know what you're doing.

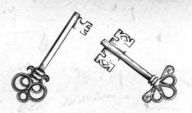

KEYS IN A BOTTLE

The volunteer is a stooge, and there is another assistant hidden in the group as well. Once the bottle has been shown around, the magician holds it somewhere out of sight, and the second assistant surreptitiously changes it with a prepared bottle that already holds a duplicate of the set of keys that the stooge has. While pretending to push the keys through the bottle, the magician just palms the set the stooge gave him, tucking them into a small pocket inside his sleeve. All that then remains is for the stooge to agree that yes, this duplicate set of keys really is the original. Because the two sets look identical, the crowd believes it readily.

THE ESCAPE
Part Four

Q is Bess Houdini, Harry's wife. Although there are plenty of hints to her life to be found throughout the gazebo – her gender, her Brooklyn birthplace, her work in the *Floral Girls*, her parental nationality of German, her propensity to make Harry's costumes, and her interests in pets and dolls, the main clue is in the puzzle text. Take the first letter of each paragraph after Q's letter, and you will find that they spell out "I AM BESS H".